Body Mind and Music

Revised and Expanded Edition

Laurie Riley, CMP, CCM

www.laurieriley.com

Distributed by Harps Nouveau, 1900 S. Broadway, Denver, CO 80210 www.kolacnymusic.com/nouveau

<u>Disclaimer</u>: This book does not comprise the entirety of training for therapeutic musicians.

<u>Acknowledgements:</u> As the years have passed since the first edition of this book was printed, the number of people who should be acknowledged for their encouragement and support has grown to more than can be listed. To all of these people, know you are appreciated beyond measure.

In loving memory of my father and mother and in gratitude for their influence on my life and work.

Contents

Music is Our Birthright

Music is the birthright of humanity. It is something we are all born to.

Making music can be enlightening and joyful. We have the right to sing, dance, and play music any way we want to. And, of course, taking lessons and/or going to music school will greatly enhance our skills.

Music is extremely powerful, yet our culture deals with it as though it were akin to a hobby like stamp collecting. We tend to think of it as something we do, when in fact it is much more - it is something we *are*. We have more capacity for making music than just about anything else. The only thing holding us back is our belief system.

Toddlers sing and dance as a sheer expression of the joy of being alive, until someone tells them they have to do it a certain way, or that they are not doing it "right". Herein lies a key to whether or not we believe we are musicians.

My students often ask me, "How long will it take for me to learn to play my instrument?" I tell them, "As long as you believe it will." We are products of our assumptions and our past experiences. Part of my job as a teacher is to undo the damage done by earlier negative experiences before the student can actually begin to learn.

I'm not musically inclined and *I don't have the gift* are phrases that are universally inaccurate. We *all* have the gift. Granted, the earlier we start the easier it is, but it's never too late to begin playing or singing.

Those who grow up in musical families seem to have the easiest time learning to play and sing. They don't necessarily have more talent; they have earlier experience. Even listening is experience. In fact, it's the most important experience.

If a family does not engage in musical activity often, but a child wants to play an instrument, the lack of support he or she may experience can create limitations. Even if the parents encourage the child to practice, if they are not playing music themselves, there is less incentive and inspiration.

Some families never listen to or engage in music. For children who grow up in such families, how would they know what a note is, what pitch is, what a melody is, what harmony is? Such children are sometimes called "tone deaf". It's not a lack of talent that creates these limitations. It's lack of exposure.

The good news is that lack of early exposure or experience can be overcome.

Music enhances our brain's ability to learn. It is basic to what we are and it is tied to all our functions. Don Campbell[1], in his book *The Mozart Effect*, addressed this subject in detail. The studies he cited were done only with classical music, however, so his book appears to state that only classical music is helpful; the truth is that there are many kinds of music that are beneficial to the development of neural pathways.

The human brain likes rhythms and patterns. Remember learning the alphabet? It seemed a formidable task until we put it to a melody and a rhythm - then it became unforgettable. You can probably still sing the alphabet song today. The more rhythmic, the easier something is to learn. Even the musical scales and exercises we practice when taking lessons are easier when given a lilt or rhythm. This is because we *are* rhythm. Our cells, our molecules, our atoms, our quantum particles all vibrate with the aliveness of rhythm; without it we are, literally, dead. Most of our vital signs are expressed in rhythmic terms: brain wave, heart beat, pulse, and so on.

The fact that we are alive is the only proof we need that we are musical. Not to express it is to deny our aliveness. Not allowing oneself to be musical can actually have negative consequences, while expressing our musicality is beneficial.

Music and the Brain

The brain at birth has more neurons than it can ever use, and we can never feed it as much information as it is capable of handling. Before and at birth, millions of neurons are present, waiting for information to be stored and utilized. If information is strong enough (as in trauma) or repeated a few times (minimum of three) it becomes permanently stored. Some kinds of information will be "filed" in the "back of the file cabinet" if it does not get used, but it will always be there for recall.

Early learning happens without any conscious effort on the part of the infant. Babies simply absorb information. Luckily, it is impossible for a child to receive too much information. The brain will automatically sort what it does and does not need to store. (Later in life, the feeling of overwhelm we get when faced with too much input is usually caused by trying to process it consciously instead of just letting it be absorbed the way an infant does.)

In the infant brain, there are more neural pathways than can be used. Any that do not get used in early childhood begin to atrophy. By the age of ten, most neural pathways that have not been used have disintegrated. From then on, information requires a slightly longer time to be absorbed and made permanent, because new neural pathways must be created to accommodate it.

In adulthood, we can still learn easily if we don't short-circuit the process by trying too hard to make it happen; the conscious mind can only process so much at a time, while the subconscious can spontaneously process a great deal more. (In Jungian terms, we have a conscious and an *un*conscious. I prefer the term *sub*conscious, because it is not a lack of consciousness, it's a hidden consciousness. When we learn to use it well, it becomes a *hyper*consciousness.)

The subconscious is actually the larger part of our functioning. Without it we'd be helpless; we would not even be able to tie our shoes. There is no way that we can use just the conscious part of our minds to learn the enormous quantity of information required to do even the simplest tasks.

Each of us lives in two worlds, the conscious and the subconscious, yet most of us only recognize the conscious and try to filter everything through it. We think the conscious mind is reality. But the subconscious is much larger, more powerful, deeper, and a great deal more accurate. These two "worlds" are not a dichotomy. They are an integrated whole. If we will use our minds the way they are meant to be used, the way an infant learns, the way of least resistance, we can achieve greatness.

In old age, learning can slow down if we are not properly nourished. Our diet requires nutrients the brain uses, and many older people's diets are not optimal. We are never too old to learn, as is commonly thought. New neural pathways can be formed at any age. It has been found that even when the brain has been damaged, it can build new neural pathways to re-learn information that has been lost.

At any age, stimulation develops the brain. But if we give the brain insufficient stimulation in any area, it will atrophy in related skills. It has been found that the relative size of an adult brain is related to the amount of stimulus it receives.

Conscious and subconscious shouldn't be confused with left and right brain functions. The subconscious includes both. The right side of the brain is said to process intuitive, emotional, and creative skills, language and music, pattern recognition, and recall of idealogic knowledge. The left side processes logical, analytic, sequential and linear thinking, and recall of factual information. We may be inclined toward one side or the other, but neither is better than the other. We can balance both sides of the brain if we wish to do so by purposely using all the functions mentioned above, and this enhances the quality of our life and our learning.

The overly "right-brained" person can be very creative and intuitive, but annoyingly unreliable and unrealistic. The overly "left-brained" person can be logically adept and have a spectacular grasp of facts and data, but can lack creative skills and even social skills. Each might think the other's skills to be unnecessary and unimportant, and may make no attempt to become more balanced. But if we can make the effort to develop skills for both sides of the brain, we can achieve true brilliance.

Music is a Language

Processing Music

Some research has indicated that when we actively (rather than passively) listen to music - in other words, when we pay attention to the music we hear - it is processed in the same area of the brain as language. The same is true when we learn music by ear. In all respects, music is a language.

Learning music from notation without much prior listening and participatory exposure forces us to use a part of the brain which is not well suited for this task: the part that processes mathematics. Although music and mathematics are intimately related (see my book *Singing the Universe Awake*[2]), each requires a very different learning process if music is to be played in a way that is more than robotic.

Tribal cultures have always, and still do, use music as part of everyday life; everyone sings or dances or plays, rather than leaving it only to a certain few. Complex rhythms are often used in tribal music, and these undoubtedly develop the brain in ways that make music easy and natural.

Beyond innate music skills, we tend to think that advanced skills should develop more quickly than they do. But how long does it take to learn good *language* skills? We learn most of our language in the first few years of life, but in early childhood we speak in a way that is far from skilled. By the time we are seven or eight we are doing much better, and soon we begin to experiment with subtleties such as slang and humor. By the time we are in our late teens, if we've had a reasonably good education, we can understand most of what we read where vocabulary and phrasing are concerned. In other words, it takes a long time to learn advanced language skills. Music is no different.

Now imagine what would happen to a child learning to speak without the stimulation of hearing adults speaking. If we don't hear language spoken we cannot learn it. First a toddler makes noises and has fun with them. Over time he or she gains control over the sounds, and begins to recognize that adults and older siblings are using specific sounds to convey meaning. As the child tries to master this, mistakes are made, but no matter. The process is natural and stress-free. No one is judging, least of all the child.

Now imagine a toddler being told, "No, no, you must not speak until you can read and write." By the time that's accomplished, the child's ability to speak would be stunted forever. Language cannot be learned effectively just from the written page. It has to be heard, mimicked, and experimented with before it becomes coherent, and we must be able to speak before we read and write. Yet we expect to learn music from the written page alone, and we're told it's wrong to learn it by ear!

And what if a babbling toddler were told, "Those noises are wrong. Don't make any noise unless it's a word." This would be impossible. The child would give up and never speak. Yet this is exactly what we are told about learning music - not to play with or experiment with musical sounds, but to play only structured tunes, exercises and pieces. Is it any wonder that so many people give up on learning music?

Language conveys ideas, moods, emotions, and images. It is not just the word, phrase, or sentence that conveys the meaning; it is how it is expressed when spoken, using tone of voice and dynamics. Music is precisely the same; it is not just the notes and measures that make it a language, but how it is expressed.

If at our first music lesson, the teacher opens a book, sets it on the music stand, and proclaims, "Here is the music," we could get the impression that everything that is important is on the page. Well, you could listen all day to that book and never hear any music. The page itself is silent. There is no music there. What is there is a tool from which music can be brought forth. Music is so much more than just a series of notes!

Repertoire: the Vocabulary of the Language of Music

Memorizing

When repertoire is memorized, not only do you have it forever, but it is easily accessed, and you are much more free to put all your creative energy into your playing or singing. With no third party (notation) between you and your instrument, your attention can be more focused.

Memorization seems daunting to many musicians, yet in fact it is easy and natural. The only reason it seems difficult is because a large number of otherwise skilled musicians have never been taught how. Before there was musical notation - only a few hundred years ago - everything was either memorized or improvised. The bards of Europe and griots of Africa could memorize songs and poems that were several hours long, word for word. What we don't practice and experience, we don't realize can be valuable.

Do you carry your repertoire in a tote bag? Can you truly say that you *know* the music you play? Obviously, orchestral players and those who work in clubs, restaurants, or do studio work need a repertoire so vast that notation and/or charts are necessary, so being able to sight-read is a necessary skill. But for other situations, such as solo concerts, small ensemble playing, therapeutic music, and social music-making, dependence on notation can hinder us.

For every gig, carrying around a bag of music books, setting up the music stand, finding the pieces you plan to play or sing, referring to the notation every few seconds, turning pages, and so on, is a bit like building a piano that has to be reconstructed each time it's played. Picture this: to play this piano, you'd have to take it out of a crate in pieces, get out your screwdriver and hammer, put it together, string it up and tune it before every practice or performance. Why not just build it permanently? Likewise, why not memorize your repertoire, so you need no props?

Contrary to common thought, memorizing does not mean "seeing the notes in your head". If you memorize the way the notes look on a page, you still have to "read" them in your head to play them, so the actual notation may as well be used. And this kind of memorizing *is* more difficult.

Nor is it practical to try to memorize a piece by reading it through in its entirety all at once. Memorizing is more easily done a bit at a time. You wouldn't take a meal on a plate, dump it down your throat in one big mass, and hope to digest it.

First, just look at the notation and notice the patterns of the melody and the accompaniment. Notice the time signature and count the first phrase aloud. Notice the key.

Next, play or sing that phrase and *only* that phrase. At this point, tempo is not important; playing should be very slow no matter what tempo you will eventually work up to. Listen to the music's patterns and "shapes". Observe your hand placements and fingerings on the instrument and remember those visual patterns as well. Play or sing the phrase over and over until you develop "muscle memory" and can also hum it to yourself. Then try doing it with your eyes closed.

Memorize the piece phrase by phrase. Practice each phrase separately and thoroughly before putting them together. For instance, after you have memorized the first phrase, put it aside and memorize just the second phrase until you know it well. Then play both phrases together.

Some musicians prefer to memorize the last phrase first and work forward. Whichever you do, be sure you memorize them all equally well. Then put them all together into a unified whole.

When a piece is truly memorized, if you make a mistake you won't have to go back to the beginning and start over; you will be able to pick it up anywhere or to simply play through the "unexpected notes". Also, if you have truly memorized a piece, you should be able to play it at any tempo - from very slow to much too fast - equally well. Of course, you'll perform it in the correct tempo.

One of the most common mistakes we musicians make is to try to make a piece we're learning sound musical right away. This shortcuts all the precise attention it needs to the detail that gives it character and accuracy. Keep the tempo slow and let it be a work in progress for as long as it takes. Don't force it.

Everyone has the ability to memorize. If you haven't had luck with it, it's not a lack of ability but a lack of training in how to do it. The musician who can play or sing well from notation *and* from memory has a definite advantage, and I believe our musical training should include both.

How to memorize your music:

1. Count and read through a piece before playing
2. Observe patterns
3. Observe intervals within the patterns and phrases
4. Remember chord sequences
5. Practice by repetition of short phrases
6. "Hear" the music in your head
7. Hum the music
8. Observe your fingerings
9. Trust muscle memory
10. Don't go back to the beginning when you make a mistake

11. Play along with a recording, or record yourself playing from the notation and then play along with that (without reading the notation while you play along).
12. Play it at every tempo from very slow to very fast

Repertoire Lists

If someone asked you for your repertoire, could you give them a definitive list? Many of us draw a blank after naming a few pieces, even though we know many. Do you have to dig through your music books or binder to find your repertoire? It's quite a chore. There is an easier way!

Take some time to go through your sources and make a coherent list of every piece you play or sing well. Divide the list into categories such as keys, composers or styles. If all your music is memorized, the repertoire list is a necessity even if the notation isn't.

Beyond that, you can keep copies of every piece in protective plastic pages in an organized binder. (Xeroxing music for your own purposes is not against the law; copyright applies to copying it for others or selling it). The table of contents you create becomes your repertoire list. If you don't think of yourself as organized, this is your chance!

Mastering Styles

There are myriad musical styles - pop, jazz, classical, Celtic, Medieval, baroque, folk, blues, liturgical, country, New Age, swing, rock, a host of ethnic styles - the list goes on and on. These are the dialects of the language of music.

There are so many styles that one musician can never master them all, and being good at one style of music doesn't necessarily make us good at another. There is a different set of skills and a different way of thinking for each style of music. We can't apply one paradigm to another. Look at what happens, for instance, when a folksinger tries opera. But before laughing too hard, consider the opposite! It's not a skill issue - it's a stylistic one.

Because of the complexity of nuance involved in each musical style, we can't learn a style from the notation alone. If you just play the notes, it's like knowing how to pronounce the words of a foreign language without knowing their meaning. You could read it from a book, but you wouldn't know what you were saying, could not express it properly or emphasize the right syllables and words. You wouldn't be able to *communicate*.

We have to listen often to a style we wish to learn, played on appropriate instruments and/or sung by those who specialize in that style. We can then absorb it over time, as we would any language.

When we don't know a style, we may not really hear what's going on. For instance, what may seem stylistically simple at first may later reveal itself as quite complex as you begin to understand it. A good example is Celtic music; considered "simple" by musicians listening for melodic complexity, they may not notice the variety of ornaments and the syncopated rhythms used by masters of the style. Another example is South American music, which is often melodically basic, but uses polyrhythms that require a whole new way of thinking.

Of course, if you're a soloist, you have the right to make any kind of music any way you wish to, but it behooves us to choose to follow or break the rules of any given style from a place of knowledge. It is enriching to learn as much as possible about whatever styles of music we wish to play.

Sight Reading

If we were only allowed to read to others from books we had already read before, very little reading would be done out loud. We can, and often do, read to others what we are reading for the first time ourselves. In music, sight reading is comparable.

Being able to read quickly and accurately from notation we've not seen before enables us to play more music than we've practiced and learned. There are some excellent sight-readers, but not all of us have that skill because we've not been taught some of the secrets.

One of the slowest ways to read music is to think of the name of every note. Reciting note names in your head takes time and effort that gets in the way of playing. We don't, for instance, spell out every word letter by letter as we read a book. We read words as whole entities. Likewise, we can learn to recognize intervals, patterns, and chord forms in notation. This makes sight reading possible, and it also makes us better musicians.

Sight reading is a skill you can learn from a good teacher, when your basic music-reading skills are in place.

"Fake Books"

When speaking in public, rather than reading verbatim from a prepared speech, it's more effective to use an outline, and to improvise one's words from that. In music, the parallel to this is the "fake book", a bridge between sight reading and improvising. It's a useful tool for those who need to have a very large repertoire at hand, and there are fake books for every style. They provide notation for the melody, and the names of accompanying chords, so you can read the melody and improvise the accompaniment. Ask at your local music store for Fake Books in your chosen style of music.

Basic Music Terminology

What is a melody? A melody is a sequence of notes that create a complete musical "story".

What is a tune? A tune is melody with no lyrics.

What is a song? A song is a tune with lyrics that are sung.

What is a "piece"? A "piece" is a selection of music, which may be a tune, a song, or a longer composition.

What is harmony? Harmony is created by additional notes that accompany a melody.

What are chords? A chord is three or more notes sounding together, creating harmony.

*What is a scale?*A scale is a progressive set of notes. For instance, the major scale that starts on the C note progresses thusly: C, D, E, F, G, A, B, and C.

What is an interval? When two notes are played at the same time or sung consecutively, the term "interval" refers to the distance between them. For instance, choose a note and call it "one", and then choose another note and count how many notes there are between the two, *including both of the notes you've chosen.* The number you count is the interval. If, for instance, there are five notes, the interval is a *fifth.* If there are three notes, it's a *third.* And so on.

What is notation? Note symbols printed on a music staff are called "notation". (See the section *How to Read Music.*) Notation is often also referred to as "the music", although they're actually just symbols for music; the real music is what you make when you play!

What is an exercise? An exercise is used for the purpose of becoming accustomed to certain sequences, patterns, and techniques. Practicing exercises is absolutely essential to becoming a good musician.

What is a phrase? A phrase is a group of notes that complete a musical thought, much like the words between commas in a written sentence.

What is repertoire? A repertoire is a collection of tunes that you know and can play or sing well. Every musician works to develop a repertoire.

Beyond terminology, having a working knowledge of music theory is more helpful than many musicians realize. The term "music theory" seems so dry, and the way it's often taught certainly makes it so. I took a theory course in college, which was presented on the blackboard instead of on instruments. I was unable to apply it to my instrument as a result.

If you browse the web for "music theory", you'll come up with websites which state that theory is all about reading music notation. But in actuality, music theory is what you use whenever you play an instrument, whether from notation, memorized, or by ear.

Music theory is actually fascinating, fun, and very usable. Knowing the principles of basic music theory *as they apply to your instrument* (or to singing) makes playing (or singing) easier. A working knowledge of theory also makes improvisation more natural.

Once you know why your instrument works the way it does, a good theory course will make much more sense. The more you can learn about the language and structures of music, the better musician you will be.

Concert Pitch

Concert pitch is the pitch to which modern musicians agree to tune their instruments so they may be played in ensemble.

In Medieval times, concert pitch was based on the Middle A note being 417 Hz (Hertz, cycles per second). Over time, as audience sizes grew and concert halls got bigger, instruments were tuned higher to be perceived as louder, and currently A 440 is considered concert pitch. Some orchestras actually tune even higher.

Harmonics and How the Do-Re-Mi Scale Came to Be

Harmonics are overtones produced by a vibrating string. You can hear harmonics by very lightly touching a harp or guitar string at certain places along its length and plucking the string. For instance, if you touch a string very lightly with one finger at exactly ½ its length and pluck it at the same time with another finger, you will hear a note exactly one octave higher than the open string. That's because lightly touching the string has interrupted the wave pattern produced by the pluck; it has "shortened" the string's vibrating length by ½. If you touch the string at ¼ its length, you will hear a note 2 octaves higher than the open string, and at 1/8 you will hear a note 3 octaves higher. If you touch the string at 1/3 its length, you will hear the 5th. At 1/6 its length you will hear a fifth plus an octave. And so on. Under perfect circumstances you would hear all the intervals.

When these harmonic overtone pitches are set up in sequence from lowest to highest, the result is the 7-tone (diatonic or do-re-mi) scale.

On a piano keyboard, the white keys are a *diatonic* (do-re-mi) scale, and a span of 8 keys is an octave. (The diatonic is called the

7-tone scale, and that can be confusing - it refers to all the notes except the octave note.)

Adding the black keys of the piano, you then have a *chromatic* (12-tone) scale. (Again, the 12 tones do not include the octave.) Each note in a chromatic scale is a half-step higher than the previous note.

Key Changes and the Succession of Fifths

The next chart shows the succession of each musical key and its relationship to the succession of 5ths. In the chart, two octaves of the diatonic (do-re-mi) scale are represented on the top horizontal line. Each vertical line represents a note. Each heavy vertical line represents a sharped note. The names of the scales are at the right of the chart, and each scale is represented by a horizontal line. Notice that all the notes in the C scale as represented on the top line are natural (not sharped), and that the G scale has the F's sharped, the D scale has the F's and C's sharped, the A scale has the F's, C's and G's sharped - and so on. Notice that the progression of sharps is in intervals of fifths (C to G, G to D, D to A, etc.) and the names of scales thus created by sharping notes in that succession also progress in fifths.

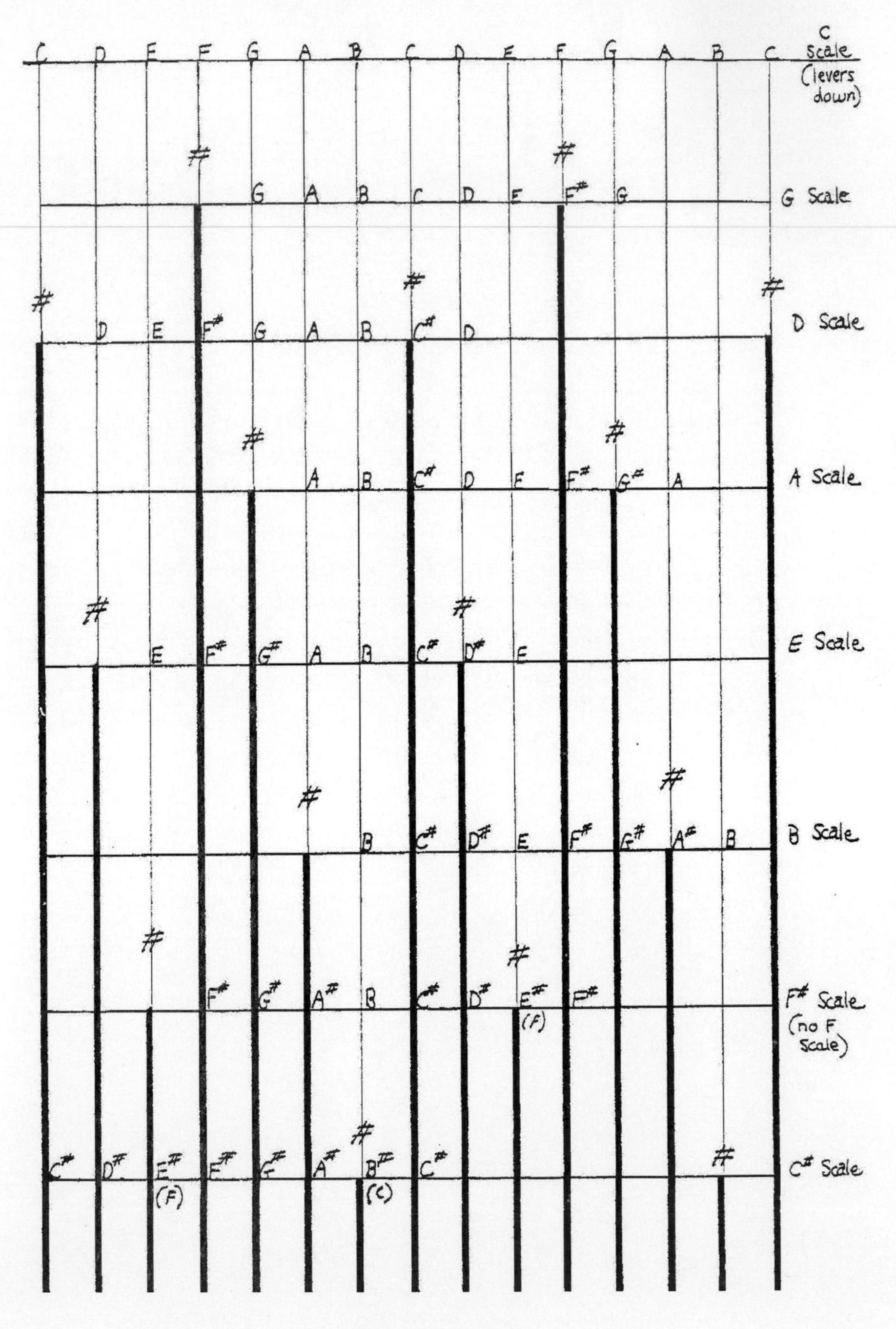
C D E F G A B C D E F G A B C
C scale (levers down)
G A B C D E F# G
G Scale
D E F# G A B C# D
D Scale
A B C# D E F# G# A
A Scale
E F# G# A B C# D# E
E Scale
B C# D# E F# G# A# B
B Scale
F# G# A# B C# D# E# (F) F#
F# Scale (no F Scale)
C# D# E# (F) F# G# A# B# (C) C#
C# Scale

Tuning Isn't Perfect

When we tune each successive note of the 12-tone scale perfectly in relation to the note before it (the frequency of the previous note x 1.05946), one might think we should arrive at perfect octaves, but in fact we don't, and we shouldn't - we actually arrive at octaves that are flat by 98.65603 %.

When we tune an instrument to mathematically perfect octaves (each octave being double the cycles per second of the previous octave), we must then tune all the notes within the octave slightly sharp to each other successively. Our modern ears are accustomed to this "tempered tuning". But when we tune a musical instrument with all octaves slightly flat because the notes between the octaves are perfectly in tune with each other successively, we achieve "mean tuning". Mean tuning was commonly used during the Middle Ages, and is now sometimes used by musicians who play historical instruments and are purposely recreating the sound and feel of Medieval music.

Neither tuning is perfect; they are both compromises. It is also why musical instruments can never be perfectly tuned. Many musicians with very sensitive ears can tune very accurately but still hear the discrepancy.

Practice is Passion

What is talent?

How nice it would be if we could just automatically be good musicians, with no practice involved; just sit down and play brilliantly!

The concept of talent came from the idea that there are a select few for whom music comes naturally. Since good musicians invest a great deal of time and energy in their music, the concept of talent is quite unfair, and when someone says, “My, what talent you have,” it’s rather insulting. Making music well *doesn’t* just happen. It requires patience and much practice.

Talent is actually a result of an accumulation of experience. It may come early if we listen to and play music early in life. Or it can come later, whenever we choose to immerse ourselves in music and integrate it into our consciousness. Above that, the key to good musicianship is practice.

Practice Methods

Many musicians have a love-hate relationship with practice. We love the results, but instead of enjoying practice, we stress over it. We don’t hear ourselves making beautiful music, because we’re focused on the eventual outcome instead.

If you wish to be the master of your music, *hear your music*. When you hear it, you can express it. When you can express it, you are much closer to your goal. Forcing it won’t help, but enjoying the process will. If you are playing or singing exercises, revel in the patterns and feelings of them. If you are doing simple tunes, absorb the beauty of each note. If you are going for complexity, love the challenge.

Did you know that a relaxed practice session will produce the same benefits as meditating, and the resulting production of endorphins in the brain leads to better health and better moods?

If we have good practice habits, we can trust the process of practicing, to know that when we practice well the results will be good.

If you don't enjoy the music you're learning, let your teacher know. Music is supposed to be fun. It is not just another job to be done like taking out the garbage. Choose pieces that excite you!

Practice produces the best results when we practice every day. You can do several short sessions per day: five, ten, twenty minutes at a time. Or you can do a longer session; an hour or two (with short breaks every 20 minutes or so), but no more. The brain does not absorb over-practice. How long you practice at one time is not nearly as important as practicing often.

If I don't practice enough, I feel nervous on stage. Without enough practice, there is no assurance I'll play as well as I want to, and then the concentration required just to be sure I hit all the right notes prevents me from being able to make the music truly expressive.

Practicing and performing usually involve two different states of mind. In performance, we are often concentrating on every detail, while practicing pieces we know well is often done on "automatic pilot". Then when you perform, it feels different because of the disparity in states of mind. To perform well, it helps to practice not only the music but the state of mind you will be in when you perform.

Aural, Kinesthetic and Visual Learning

Being aware of whether you are an aural, visual, or kinesthetic learner is helpful. If you're an aural learner, you remember best what you hear. If a visual learner, you remember best what you see. If a kinesthetic learner, you remember best what you experience physically, such as patterned movements.

Think of this in regard to memorizing phone numbers, for instance. An aural learner will have to say the numbers before dialing. A visual learner will "see" the numbers in the mind, as though they were on paper. A kinesthetic learner might not say the numbers or even visualize them, but the fingers will dial them automatically.

We usually give the most credence to whichever way we learn most easily, unless someone has forbidden us to do so. If we run into trouble with a teacher, it's often because their favorite way of teaching is not our best way of learning.

Ideally, we learn best when we learn all three ways, even if it takes a little extra effort. The more ways we can set the knowledge on our neural pathways, the more thoroughly it will be understood and absorbed, and the longer it will stay there.

Overcoming Blocks to Musical Progress

Many musicians are never completely satisfied with their musicianship, and many students are never satisfied with their progress. We may become frustrated when things seem difficult. We all have blocks somewhere, which may be technical or psychological.

Here are some of the symptoms of technical blocks:

1. Lack of progress and musical growth
2. Hitting a “plateau” you can’t seem to get beyond
3. Lack of accuracy not corrected by more practice
4. Poor rhythm and/or unsteady tempo
5. Poor tone
6. Lack of expression
7. Inability to memorize

You may not be aware when you have some of the above problems. It’s a good idea to have your playing assessed for these qualities by an unbiased professional.

Here are some of the symptoms of psychological blocks:

1. Lack of inspiration and direction
2. Boredom or apathy, no desire to play or practice
3. Lack of concentration
4. Mental blanks - forgetting what comes next or what you were doing
5. Not enough time to practice
6. Perfectionism
7. Frustration
8. Stage Fright

Let’s look at the causes and solutions for both sets of symptoms:

- *Lack of progress and musical growth* is usually caused by poor practice habits, and not having good examples to aspire to so you can imagine what your music could sound like. Seek advice from professional musicians on their practice habits. Find recordings of excellent singers or players of your instrument, and listen often, noting specifically what they do that you want to be able to do. Talk with your teacher to set specific goals.

- *Hitting a "plateau" you can't seem to get beyond* happens to most of us at some point. If you can't imagine what more you could be doing, a solution is to take a workshop or lesson with a professional you have not studied with before, to learn new skills you've not been exposed to previously.

- *Lack of accuracy not corrected by more practice* can happen when practice methods are ineffective. When there is a problem area in a piece you're practicing, use the measure or phrase as an exercise (do it over and over) until it has improved. If you play a stringed instrument and this problem does not resolve using this method, poor fingering is usually the culprit. Even if the fingering is indicated in the notation, it may not be right for *you*, and you may have to re-work it. If you still have accuracy troubles, get a metronome and use it; you'll be amazed at how much better you will play after just a few sessions. Neurologically, we respond to the steady click; which enhances music learning.

- *Poor rhythm and/or unsteady* tempo results from not using a metronome in practice. This tool is essential. Use it. (Get one that clicks rather than beeps; it's hard to hear beeps when you're playing or singing.)

- *Poor tone* results from poor technique. If you are getting, say, a $300 tone out of a $3000 instrument, seek professional advice to improve your tone production. Often, we tend to play softly because we don't want to disturb others, or don't want our potential mistakes to be heard - these habits are not conducive to good tone-production. Always pay attention to bringing out the best sound your instrument can make.

- *Lack of expression* is usually caused by over-concentration on what you already know how to do habitually. Once you have learned and practiced a piece well, concentrate on expression.

Expression is modulation of tone and accenting of passages and notes to make the music "speak" eloquently.

- *Inability to memorize* is simply a result of not having been taught how to memorize! It's not an inherent talent but a learned skill, and anyone can do it. This skill is addressed elsewhere in this book.

- *Lack of inspiration and direction, boredom and/or apathy, and/or no desire to play or practice* often come from doing music you don't enjoy. If there is a style of music that excites you, that's the style you should study! And you should get plenty of recordings by experts in that field, and listen often.

- *Lack of concentration, inability to relax, and mental blanks* get in the way of good practice and progress. These are caused by not clearing other concerns from your mind at practice time. A good solution is to create a daily schedule on which all your activities are mapped out and a specific amount of time is allotted to each. In this way, you can give your full attention to each activity in your day. Also, you may be filling up your time on unnecessary things. Make a list of everything you do in a typical day. Then assign a value to each activity, from 1 to 10, with 10 being most important. Then eliminate everything that doesn't have a value of at least 5, and make a daily schedule for the remaining activities, with a timeline, and follow it! If music is important to you, you will make time for it.

- *Stage Fright* is fear that causes us to "mess up" in the ways we fear we will. Interestingly, if you weren't afraid, you wouldn't mess up as much. Prime causes are lack of adequate practice, not knowing how to play or sing through your mistakes, and not being accustomed to being the center of attention. If you haven't practiced your music so thoroughly that you can do it well under any kind of stress, don't perform it yet! Most people think professionals perform perfectly. In fact, most don't - they simply know how to get through their mistakes seamlessly; therefore audiences are usually unaware that any mistakes have occurred. Stage fright can give the appearance during performance that we haven't the skills we had at home. Therefore, overcoming stage fright is important. The simplest way to overcome it is to practice until there is no question you know your music exquisitely well. Then gradually put yourself in situations that are more and more demanding; all the lesser ones will seem easy by comparison. Before a performance, meditate or do relaxation exercises. I also like to observe my audiences as they arrive and are seated (from a vantage point where they can't see me watching) so that I feel I "know" them before I perform for them. Another calming method is to concentrate on expression; this leaves no room for fear. If you have severe intractable stage fright, hypnotherapy may be helpful.

- *Not enough practice* leads to insecurity and poor performance. Therefore, practicing every day is important.

- *Perfectionism*, believe it or not, can be as limiting as not practicing. Perfectionism is the idea that everything we do must be done right or not at all. Since learning an instrument consists primarily of making mistakes and then correcting them, practice can become incredibly frustrating for the perfectionist, if you expect yourself to play perfectly when you don't yet know the pieces. What could be more unreasonable than that? Consider that a large jetliner's autopilot system simply makes a constant series of corrections to keep the plane on target. That's exactly what practice is. It's important to allow yourself to play imperfectly when you're first learning a piece of music. It's also important to learn how to play through errors, which *will* occur, and to forgive yourself for them. There's plenty of good music that happens between them! Keep in mind that when you hear a recording it sounds perfect, but studio engineering created that, not the musician. For live music, I like this motto: *Strive for beauty, not perfection.*

- *Frustration,* besides being a result of perfectionism, can also result from being expected to play or sing music that is beyond your present skill level. If you feel the music is too difficult, be sure to express this to your teacher, and learn simpler music until your skills grow.

There are more reasons and solutions for lack of musical progress, as follows:

- A student may have a *lack of a realistic idea of the commitment required.* I've often had students who expected to learn in a week what should take a year to learn well.

- Many potentially good musicians don't believe in their own abilities. *Belief* is the strongest factor in how much progress we make, and it colors the entire experience of making music. Know that your ability is no less than anyone else's, including those who are very successful. They didn't get that way through chance, but through consistent work and integrity.

- *Not having the right instrument* can be one of the biggest blocks to musical progress. Are you playing the instrument you want to be playing? Is it of good quality, with a pleasing tone? I recall having a terrible guitar as a kid. I wanted to learn it, but it was unplayable. Beginners need good instruments.

- *Using a method not suited to you* is a common problem. Do your hands and body feel comfortable while playing your instrument? If singing, does your voice feel natural and unstrained? If not, you may need to use a different technique. If there is discomfort, lack of progress, poor tone, etc., something is wrong. "No pain no gain" is a dangerous myth, both psychologically and physically.

- *Lack of willingness to use proper technique* is the opposite problem from the one above, and it's just as damaging to progress. Many students want to make music instantly, and think technique gets in the way, and they soon find themselves making no progress.

- *Poor Ergonomics (poor posture and/or playing position)* can cause enough physical discomfort to discourage a musician. (See the next chapter, "The Musician's Body".)

- *Lack of self-nurturing* is a limiting factor in musical progress, especially for those who take care of everyone else but themselves. I recommend reading Thomas Moore's *Care of the Soul*[37]. We cannot nurture others if our own resources are depleted. We need to take the time to replenish our energy and enthusiasm.

- *Not defining your goals:* how can you know how to get there if you've never decided where you're going? Take the time to sit down and think through what you want. Allow yourself to fantasize; if people only did what they or others thought was realistic and practical, we'd still be in the stone age. List your goals and aspirations. Then give each item a value from 1 to 10, with 10 being what you want most. Then omit the items with a value lower than 5. Next, write down a plan for achieving the goals remaining on your list. Post the list on your refrigerator or in some visible place where you are constantly reminded of your plan.

- *Being unaware that the learning process never ends!* There is no one, no matter what level of mastery they have achieved, who feels they have nothing more to learn, unless they are hopelessly unrealistic. There is no end point at which one eventually arrives. Learning is lifelong.

Inspiration and Practicality

We are physical, mental, emotional and spiritual beings. What we learn in music study is not just skill, for that addresses only the physical and mental. If we are to satisfy the emotional and spiritual parts of our being, we also need inspiration.

We cannot help but be affected by the conscious and subconscious experiences in our past that can influence our music both positively and negatively. Teachers' personalities, what people said, and how we judge ourselves are all factors that can color our present experience and also determine how we handle perceived successes and failures. Making room for inspiration can tip the balance of past and present experiences into transformative ones.

The original meaning of the word *inspiration* was to *breathe in.* The "spire" part of the word is derived from *spirit.* In other words, inspiring is infusing ourselves with spirit - one's own spirit, divine spirit, or however you choose to interpret it.

Inspired playing is that which expresses our soul. What could be more personal than playing from the soul? And therefore, what could be more natural? Yet many of us wonder how to connect with this part of ourselves, and how to express it in our music.

There is a practice I call *Concentricity.* This word is reminiscent of *concentrate*, but it's much more. Concentricity is deep focus that accesses the core of the Self. As a musician you can make the practice of Concentricity uniquely fulfilling and beneficial.

Before each performance, I like to find a quiet place to sit and go through these steps:

1. Enter a focused or meditative state of mind.
2. Remember why I chose to become a musician.
3. Make a decision to respect my audience, and to perform with love.
4. Nurture a feeling of gratitude for being able to make music, to share it, to be of service; gratitude for the instrument(s) I own and the voice I have, all my physical senses, my hands, my brain.

Even though we may be aware of the above things on a daily basis, purposely focusing on them before each performance has a profound effect on the quality and experience of performance, and it increases the bounty of these gifts.

Emotion

Studies in mind-body sciences have indicated that memories, experiences and emotions are stored not only in the brain but in the cells of the body as well. There is no boundary between mind and body.

Music is powerfully evocative of emotions and past experiences. It is a rare person who is not touched by some style of music, and specifically by certain compositions. Emotions that arise may be perceived as positive or negative, but catharsis is almost always healing. Emotions that are not expressed are stored in the cells, where they may negatively affect our well-being. Music draws them out and helps us feel and express them.

We've been erroneously taught that expressing, or even having, certain emotions is bad. We try to avoid feeling anger, sorrow and grief. But in Bill Moyers' *Healing and the Mind* video series, certain studies cited showed that appropriate expression of both "negative" and "positive" emotions has a positive effect on the body; that it is not the emotion but the lack of expression of it, that is toxic to us.

Biophysicist Candace Pert also speaks eloquently of this in this video series, as well as in her book *The Molecules of Emotion* [16].

It is possible to learn to express "negative" emotions appropriately. As long as we do no harm to another or to ourselves, mentally or physically, expressing our emotions is essential to our wellbeing. And it is essential to our music.

The Power of Words

It has been said that words do not describe - they create. All we have to do is observe our own language and that of others to see how true this is. If you are a music teacher, surely you've heard some students say, "I can't." This belief hinders their progress. We know that how well and how quickly one learns to play music is dependent on how well and how quickly they believe they can, and those beliefs are expressed in their language. Change the language and the belief begins to change with it.

Observe your own language and you will see a direct correlation between your words and your reality. Nurture your musicianship with positive words.

Attitude

Our experience of making and of hearing music is always a function of our own attitude. What we bring to our music is what our music becomes. We create our own experience of it both consciously and subconsciously, from expectation, and from anticipation.

Let's look at some of the less positive attitudes that are common among musicians:

We seem to have a universal desire to find "The Teacher", the ultimate instructor who can, by osmosis or by some magical process, make us into exactly what they are. How many students (of anything) go from teacher to teacher, being enamored for a while until they realize the teacher is only human, and running off to find another! Or we obtain degree upon degree yet never feel ready to actually begin our life's work. I call this "perpetual studentism" or "The Impossible Guru Syndrome". If we would accept that there is no perfect teacher, we'd be able to settle down with the teachers we have.

That's not to say we should have just one teacher forever. The more teachers we have, the more we learn. But how we allow ourselves to learn from them makes all the difference in the world.

Another tendency many of us have is to look at those we think are better or more experienced than ourselves as targets for envy, to view those whose skills are equal to ours as competitors, and to consider inferior those whose skills are not as advanced as ours. These attitudes cause a sense of personal insufficiency and struggle, and cut us off from real sources of energy and inspiration. It also undermines those who can be our best cheerleaders: our peers and fellow musicians.

It's unfortunate that some music schools perpetuate competitive attitudes. In at least one famous school, piano students have to check regularly for razor blades inserted between the piano keys by other students who wish to eliminate "the competition".

At some point we have to stop comparing ourselves with others, stop being competitive, and become part of the musical community in which we support each other as equals. We have to remember why we wanted to be musicians: for the beauty of it!

Moving Into Yourself

What happens when you move from one house to another? You go through your stuff, get rid of what isn't useful to you, and move the rest to a new place, where you put it in order in a way that pleases you. Likewise, at some point in our musical development, we need to make a move; to sort through what we know, and what we've believed. We need to throw away what is not useful, and move inward with what remains. With this new clarity, we can own our musicality and knowledge and make it who we are.

In order to move into ourselves without bringing unwanted baggage along, here is a checklist of things to throw away:

1. An investment in being right. What we know, how we learned it, how it should sound, and so on, are all *flexible*. Until we recognize that there is more than one "right way", we imprison ourselves in our rightness.

2. An investment in being the only one. Others can do it too. Accept it. Support them.

3. An investment in being the best. I love the saying *Use the skills that you possess, for the woods would be a silent place if no bird sang except the best.*

4. Past Experience. The past and all that was in it is gone. Only now and the future remain. What will you do with it?

5. Expectation. If we expect things to be a specific way, what if they aren't?

Sharing Rather Than Showing

We've all been to a concert where the artist appeared to perform perfectly, had great skill, and from which we emerged saying, "That musician was great. I'll never be able to do that." We may even have noticed a lack of elation in ourselves, a lack of result of having been there. Maybe we even felt a bit discouraged.

Most of us have also been to a concert that took us to new heights of experience or depths of emotion. We emerged saying, "That musician was great. I am going to be that kind of musician." We felt eager to deepen our own music skills. And we find these concerts memorable.

What is the difference between these two kinds of performances? The former is a "see-how-good-I-am" performance. The latter is a "see-how-great-music-is" performance. One is *show*, and the other is *share*. When the performer focuses on him or herself instead of the audience, when all concentration is given to showing off impressive skills but the performer is in his or her head instead of his or her heart, you get *show*. When the performer is fully present in the moment, feeling the music, drawing it from the depths of his or her being so it can touch the listener, and connecting with the audience, you get *share*, the inspiring kind of performance that is full of life.

When we use music as a venue for self-acceptance through approval from others (a *show* performance), it's not healthy because if we fall short of what we have decided is acceptable or what we think an audience's reaction should be, we think we have failed. And if we are judgmental of ourselves, the audience follows our lead and sits in judgment of us. They pick it up subliminally. In such situations, the audience cannot relax and enjoy the performance. The end result will be that they are left cold, even if the performance was note-perfect.

A *share* performance requires self-acceptance. Acceptance is really something we can only seek from ourselves. And when we accept ourselves, our audiences do as well.

That's not to say you cannot use music as a way to build self-esteem. But this comes from integrity in developing skill rather than from the approval of others.

Imperfect Situations

In performance and in service situations such as therapeutic music sessions, if all does not go well due to extenuating circumstances, frustration can keep us from enjoying our work. We might make the mistake of assuming that challenging circumstances are rare, and it will be better next time if everyone is more cooperative or more knowledgeable. But if you look back, how many times has this sort of thing happened to you? Chances are, more often than not.

After long experience we come to see that there simply is no perfect situation. There is no way that those who are not themselves performers or service-oriented musicians can understand our needs well enough to provide for them perfectly. This reality is not going to change. Therefore, it is we who must change. Byron Katie[8] eloquently tells us, "The cause of suffering is the idea that things should be different from how they are." I think she's right. A shift in outlook can produce wonderful results. Making the very best of every situation makes the music more enjoyable for all concerned.

This isn't to say we can't inform people in advance of what our needs are, but it does mean that once we arrive, we can accept what is offered, and in return, offer our best.

Nothing Less Than Your Best

This section is about mastery, about becoming the best player or singer you can possibly be. Mastery is within your reach, because it's not about comparison with others. It's about what *you* can do rather than about what others can do.

Many of us have no idea what our best actually is. The potential for growth is actually limitless, even for those who already are seasoned professionals.

Some of us are subconsciously afraid that if we excel in something, it will become a big responsibility: we'd have to keep up appearances. But excellence does not depend on showing others what we can do; therefore no appearances are necessary. Excellence is a natural outcome of passion plus integrity.

What Is Your Passion?

If you're a musician, music is probably your passion. If it isn't, why do it? If you're doing music because someone else said you should, don't. Find your real passion and do that. Not because your music would offend someone, but because you won't be happy until you are doing what you love.

If music is your passion, do it wholeheartedly. When we ignore or put off our passion in favor of doing something else, we are not benefiting others or ourselves. We might think it's selfish to engage in our passion, but in actuality, it is selfish *not* to. Our passion is what we're *supposed* to do, or we would not have been given the desire to do it.

Why on earth do we ignore our passions by spending our lives doing something else? Most people would say it's because they can't make a living doing what they really want to do. But if that were so - and music is a good example - there would be no one at all doing it!

You might say you'd be shirking your responsibilities to your family if you engaged in your passion. But not being happy does your family no favor. When you have not fed your own heart, you can't feed others.

There are only a very few people who say they don't have a passion. For such people, it usually turns out with a little enquiry that this isn't really true. Usually the passion has simply been squelched, either by themselves or by someone else.

If you think back to earliest childhood, what drew your interest? For me, it was always art, dance, and music. But over time, music became the strongest. There was no question. I was lucky; no one ever told me I couldn't or shouldn't do it, except one nasty piano teacher. I was taught by my parents, however, that even though they supported my music-making I had to learn to make a living some other way, and that was where I faltered. I had a terrible time making a living during my early adult life, doing what I was "supposed" to do. I tried many kinds of "responsible" jobs, hating them all and not making enough income anyway, and finally got tired of despising my life. I decided to go into music full time, and by burning all my bridges behind me, gave myself no alternative. (It's been said that when you have a goal *and* an alternative, you will always reach the alternative but never the goal.)

From the very first day of promoting my music as a career, I made a *much* better living than I ever had before. I loved what I was doing. My heart was in it, and that drew success to me. That is what passion is about: it ensures success.

Having one's heart in it means more than sitting in your living room expecting to be discovered. I know many a languishing musician who does that. If you want to have a career in music, you have to do the work - but the work is a pleasure when music is your passion. Making a career out of it involves doing the paperwork, phone calling, promotion, practicing, recording and marketing, and finding venues for performance.

You don't have to become a professional, of course, or do any performances at all. It's OK if you want to play music just to please yourself. Just know it's up to *you* to choose.

Whether or not you want to take your music public, you'll be happiest if you make your music the best it can be, because any lack of integrity will be known to *you*. We always know when we are not doing what we are capable of, or not giving our all to our endeavors. Do your best so you can live with yourself.

The essentials of mastery are:

- Excellent learning
- Excellent practice
- Excellent application

Excellent learning means finding the finest learning source available to you, and availing yourself of it. This does not mean that if you cannot afford the best teacher you can't study at all. It does mean utilizing what you can afford, and being truthful with yourself about that. If you can afford a latte every day or a trip to the mall on weekends, you can afford a good music teacher, good instructional DVD's and good books.

Excellent practice means finding out, rather than guessing, what actually is an effective way to practice, and doing it. Don't make it a chore. Make it a pleasure.

Excellent application means learning to do well in all situations. Whether it be on stages, therapeutic settings, or at home for yourself or your family, there are skills that help you do well - not just practice skills or how much you practice - but what you actually do physically and in your mind when you play or sing.

Doing well requires confidence, expression, relaxation, focus, integrity, and that extra something that touches souls.

The Impostor Syndrome

CEO's of large companies, stars of sports and movies, and professional musicians have something in common: a large majority suffer from something that has come to be known as The Impostor Syndrome.

I knew a talented young man who graduated Summa Cum Laude from an important music school, with a major in classical guitar. He continued to study with a famous instructor in New York City whose students' albums were in the top ten on the charts of popular music. This young man became a guitar teacher, accepting students at home. One day, he seemed depressed. I asked him what was wrong, and he replied, "I'm afraid they'll find out I'm a fake." It was a mystery to me that anyone with his accomplishments could feel that way.

Over time I learned that many top people in their fields feel the same way, and keep it to themselves as a dark secret. It is usually unfounded, of course, but they can't be convinced of that. It helps tremendously to know we are not alone in this fear, and to accept that if we have "done our homework", we are not fakes, and no one will think we are.

What we believe deeply about ourselves is a hundred percent of why and how we live and behave. It's not just how we consciously view ourselves, and certainly not entirely what we consciously tell ourselves. I used to do everything I could to give myself positive messages, but my progress in life was slow and poor. Finally, I asked myself what I saw deep in my mind's eye as the essence of "me". What I saw surprised me greatly. Instead of a capable, intelligent person (the one I consciously thought I was), I saw an image of myself as a cowering, shameful, and basically flawed being. I recognized immediately that this was who, as a very young child, I'd been told I was. Nothing I had accomplished in my life had changed this image, and I had not been aware I still carried it, yet the consequences remained. As long as I had this subconscious image, no matter how many positive affirmations I used and no matter how much recognition I got, I could never live up to my capabilities. After recognizing the existence of that image of myself and seeing it for what it was, I was able to redefine myself realistically and on purpose. I began making progress in life. I tell you this story because so many people hold unrealistic, negative images of themselves, and thus hold themselves back from doing and being their best.

Some believe deeply that they must be "humble". But not doing all we are capable of doing is a statement that says we don't want the gifts and abilities we've been given.

True humility is doing what we are meant to do, using the passion we've been given, and accepting it as our job in life, rather than rejecting it for something more "normal", more responsible, or that someone else said we should do.

I love the following quote from Marianne Williamson[39], which Nelson Mandela used in his inauguration speech:

"Our deepest fear is not that we are inadequate. Our deepest fear is that we are powerful beyond measure. It is our light, not our darkness that most frightens us. We ask ourselves, 'Who am I to be brilliant, gorgeous, talented, fabulous?' Actually, who are you *not* to be? ... Your playing small does not serve the world. There's nothing enlightened about shrinking so that other people won't feel insecure around you. We are all meant to shine, ... and as we let our own light shine, we unconsciously give other people permission to do the same. As we're liberated from our own fear, our presence automatically liberates others."

Integrity

Integrity is:

- allowing yourself to go at your own pace
- not comparing yourself to others
- not underestimating your own abilities and potential
- not overestimating or underestimating your accomplishments
- refusing to waste your time and energy on things that prevent you from achieving your goal
- not blaming anyone else for your circumstances
- committing to do whatever it takes to achieve your goal
- making no excuses

When we do not operate out of integrity, we suffer personally and musically. Suffering takes a great deal more energy than achieving does.

How can we do the things on the above list? Here's more detail:

Going at your own pace means don't set unreasonable time goals, such as when a piece of music will be performance-ready (I give most pieces a year of practice before performing them). Allow your skills time to develop.

Not comparing yourself to others includes going at your own pace, not theirs; and it also includes not feeling like their skills overshadow yours, nor yours theirs.

Likewise, *don't underestimate your abilities and potential.* Almost anyone can master music, and you are *not* the exception to that rule. Your abilities and potential are limitless.

Don't overestimate or underestimate your accomplishments. Abilities are your potential, while accomplishments are what you have achieved (regardless of your potential). Some claim rudimentary skill as superior skill - that's overestimating one's accomplishments. Although it may seem arrogant, this is actually a result of poor self-confidence. It is not uncommon to make an effort to feel better by believing one's accomplishments require no further development. But in truth, the only way to feel better is to keep progressing in skill until we achieve real excellence. If we will recognize it's OK to admit that we can make ever-greater strides, we can achieve our full potential.

If you really, really want to master your music, *refuse to waste your time and energy on things that prevent you from achieving your goal.* Compromise does not a fine musician make. The dishes and the laundry will get done, but let your music come first! Or perhaps you've given yourself a secondary hobby. That's a sneaky way to avoid practicing your music! Or maybe you habitually watch TV. It's a no-brainer to turn it off and play your music. It's more relaxing to play music than to watch TV anyway, considering what viewing violent scenes does to our endocrine and immune systems (pleasant music increases endorphins while most television programs suppress endorphins and raise cortisone levels).

While you are considering what to spend your time on, remember it's important to *not blame anyone else for your circumstances.* You are the responsible party. The past is over, the future not yet here. You are the only one with control over what you can accomplish.

Committing to do whatever it takes to achieve mastery is how people accomplish great things in life. I knew a harpist who had a prosthetic hand, and was an accomplished professional player. I've known several blind musicians who were masters. There are no excuses.

There are many masters from whom we can learn, and yet when we seek them out, we often don't follow all their advice. We pick and choose what parts of their instruction to follow, and ignore the rest. Then we wonder why we don't achieve the same level of accomplishment they have. Integrity means accepting that there are no shortcuts!

Confidence

Confidence is not just something we need for performances. We need it in our practicing as well. In fact, we need it in our lives in general. Confidence is not arrogance. It is merely the *knowing* that you can do what you have set out to do. The proof that you can is in the fact that others have done it. You have as much ability as anyone else, as long as you have the integrity to practice well. And if by chance you set out to accomplish what no one else has yet done, you can probably do that, too!

Focus and Relaxation

The mind has been said to be like a puppy that just won't do what you tell it to do, until you train it. We can train ourselves to focus. We can have "Attention Benefit" instead of "Attention Deficit".

When we relax, we can focus. When we focus, it creates further relaxation. But how do we get that circle going when we play?

1. Be sure you are seated or standing comfortably and ergonomically before starting.
2. Create a moment of silence before starting.
3. Breathe deeply, visualizing relaxation entering on the inhale, and all else but beautiful music leaving you as you exhale.
4. "Hear" the music before you play or sing it.
5. Make the first note important.

6. Imagine good tone in advance of each note.
7. Put feeling into your music.
8. Keep good tempo and rhythm when they are supposed to be there.
9. Imagine the beauty of the music flowing through your voice or instrument, out to the audience, back to you, and out again, in a circular fashion, each time becoming more beautiful.

Another technique for achieving a relaxed body and state of mind for performance is to arrive at your performance location earlier than you normally would, and after getting everything ready for your performance, find a quiet spot where others won't disturb you, and sit with your eyes closed. Visualize the stage, the lighting, your instrument, the audience, and breathe deeply. See your music as coming from the center of yourself. (If you have a spiritual practice, you can incorporate it also.) After several minutes, when you open your eyes, you'll find yourself feeling quite peaceful.

Expression

When you're concentrating on playing the right notes, how can you fully express your music? The answer lies in knowing your music *really* well. Just being able to hit all the right notes isn't really knowing it, if the intense concentration required prevents us from also having part of our consciousness free to express what we are playing or singing. Only through consistent, regular, effective practice can our music become second nature. Our fingers should be able to glide through each piece on automatic pilot, so we can stop thinking about the technicalities, and start putting some feeling in the music.

Accuracy

Expecting to be musically perfect is unrealistic - we are only human. Striving for accuracy is necessary, but gracefully handling *in*accuracy is essential.

Handling inaccuracy means that when the fingers (or the voice) don't do what you intended, you can cover it well by not flinching, not hesitating, continuing to play or sing even if the notes are not the ones you want (make something up until the right ones come back to you), and doing it all in good humor.

Once in a great while, an error gets out of control, or the memory blanks out completely. What to do? Make a joke and start again from where the error occurred (*not* from the beginning); this usually puts the audience at ease. If our intent is to please our audience, why embarrass them? Being horrified with ourselves makes them feel terrible. Let them enjoy your errors as much as your accuracies! Prepare in advance a few amusing but not self-deprecating remarks that will make them laugh.

I once heard a musician say, "With the notes that were missing from that piece, I shall now improvise this piece…"

Musical Complexity

Complexity and good performance are not necessarily related. One can make either simple or complex music and be a good performer. It's how well you do *whatever* you do, that is enjoyable to the listener. *Variety* is important, but *complexity* is optional. (Variety means having a repertoire of contrasting styles, keys, and tempos.)

I have a friend who plays dulcimer, and used to own a music shop in a tourist town. She had to play the dulcimer all day to demonstrate it to everyone who came into the store. Naturally, she became quite good at the tunes she played, which were simple ones - she didn't want to scare people out of buying a dulcimer by playing anything that sounded difficult. She never had time to learn more advanced tunes. One year she entered a presitigious national dulcimer competition, and won third place. Why was she a winner? Because what she played, she played very well, unlike many other competitors who played complex pieces they weren't really ready to perform.

Musical complexity is not a bad thing, of course. When an excellent level of skill has been attained that allows us to smoothly pull off a complex piece, that's great. Continually striving for our best can be our personal policy. There is no end to how far we can go musically. The learning never stops.

The concept of doing no less than your best is a good way to live one's entire life, as long as you accomplish this by being focused and relaxed rather than stressing. Habitually doing our best makes us feel confident, worthy, and happy. We set a good example for others. We know when we have done our best, and we know when we have not. Whenever we don't, we can forgive ourselves and go back to doing our best.

The Art of Teaching

If you are a teacher or are considering becoming one, you'll want, of course, to be the best teacher you can be. It is through integrity in teaching that your students go forth to put into practice confidently what they learn.

To be a good teacher, it's a good policy to be over-qualified: have extensive experience, education, and practice. With these qualifications, you will never have to wonder or fall prey to the Impostor Syndrome.

How can you know when you are doing a good job in your teaching?

- Know your material well
- Use a variety of learning methods
- Know a variety of techniques so you can individualize to the students' needs
- Engage students in conversation, questions, and activities
- Respect what students say and ask
- Welcome differing points of view
- Answer all questions thoroughly and politely
- Have good command of language, and use technical terminology accurately but not incessantly or condescendingly
- Have a sense of humor, smile a lot, welcome and encourage laughter
- Don't skip or gloss over basic material
- Make no assumptions about what students may already know
- Teach by sharing rather than showing

We've all had teachers who gave us a sense that their subject material required special talent to learn, and we have emerged from the classroom thinking, "I may never be able to do that".

Hopefully, we have also had teachers who took us to new heights, and we emerged saying, "I can do it!" We felt elated and eager to deepen our skills.

What is the difference between these two kinds of teachers? The former teaches from an attitude of "see how good I am". The latter teaches from "see how wonderful this information is". Just as in performance, one is *show*; the other is *share.*

If we are to assist students in touching souls with their music, their own souls must be touched first, and that can best be done by a teacher who is passionate about the material being taught, and supportive of each student's own rate of progress.

I've had some brilliant teachers and some dull ones - the dull ones taught me how *not* to teach. I always wondered why they were teaching at all; if they didn't enjoy it, how could the student? Perhaps they thought knowledge was not for enjoying.

The brilliant teachers were full of life, genuinely cared about my learning experience, and presented the material in interesting ways. I believe that anyone who cares about their students and about the material they are teaching, and who is dynamic and interactive, can pass on to their students the fire of inspiration.

It has been said that a teacher can only verbalize 50% of what he or she knows, that a student can only understand 50% of what he or she hears and can use only 50% of what he or she understands. I think this is a fair assessment. Given this dynamic, a teacher's job is challenging; one must present the material in a way that is exciting enough to capture the imaginations of students with different personalities, abilities, and attitudes.

The Five Ways of Learning

It's well known that individuals learn in at least one of five ways:

- Aural
- Verbal
- Visual
- Experiential
- Tactile

Good teaching uses all these elements in order to cover the learning needs of every student.

Aural learners retain what they have heard. They are usually good at learning music by ear. I had a history teacher who would have us read a chapter each night, and the next day he would talk about what was in the chapter. I read the chapters, but as an aural learner I learned from his telling.

Verbal learners retain what they themselves have spoken. They need to repeat or discuss what they are learning to set it in their memory.

Visual learners retain what they have seen; they may learn from reading, watching videos, demonstrations or procedures. I've heard some students say that watching videos is a waste of time, but those are usually the ones who learn best some other way.

Experiential learners have to do a specific activity to retain information, rather than just being told about, watching, or reading about it. Role-playing is a good tool for experiential learners.

Tactile learners are similar to experiential learners, with the addition that the experience must involve touch. For instance, some people can't remember telephone numbers verbally, but can dial them because their fingers know the patterns. Tactile learners often learn to play musical instruments well if not made to concentrate on the printed music as much as on the kinesthetic patterns of the music.

Every teacher needs to incorporate *all* these elements for every student. The tactile and experiential elements are covered by playing the instruments or singing; the verbal part is what you say, ask, and discuss; the aural part is the music they hear; and the visual part is what is in books as well as the melodic and harmonic patterns they see. In this way, their learning will be complete.

Teaching Private Lessons

One of the most helpful things a teacher can do for a student who takes private lessons is to become a friend. The student-teacher relationship is based on trust and respect, and what better way to gain it than to be a good friend? The friendships you develop with your students and their families can be some of the most rewarding relationships you may ever have.

Students' relationships with music is intimately linked with their relationship to their teacher. If you remain aloof and don't connect with students on deeper levels, they may never connect deeply with their music.

Being friends doesn't mean your students will have less respect for you. It means they will enjoy their learning experience more and that you, like the music they are learning, will be a part of their lives in deeper ways than just the notes they play. Being a friend to your students can actually make them better musicians.

Classroom and Workshop Teaching

Be Prepared

When teaching a workshop or class, prepare an outline beforehand. An outline is the basic structure of your talk but not the text of the talk itself. It should organize your subject material into a logical flow and timeline, and should list each part of your subject material in the order in which it will be presented.

The outline should be used as a guide, not to read from verbatim. I once had the misfortune of sitting through a class in which the teacher simply read her outline. It was meaningless and boring. The outline should simply remind you of what you *already know how to talk about in detail.*

Each section of your outline should have a time limit indicated, to help you get through everything in the allotted class time. Without a timed outline, you can find yourself only halfway through the material when it's time to end the class.

When timing your class sections, don't be looking at your watch. Instead, put a little clock where you can easily look at it without anyone noticing that you are doing so. It's annoying for students to see a teacher checking a watch or wall clock; they can misinterpret this action as meaning that you are anxious to get finished rather than that you are timing yourself for their sake.

Here is a sample of an outline for a one-hour class. (I've chosen randomly the subject of performance skills).

<u>PERFORMANCE SKILLS</u> (1 hr.)

a. Stage fright – 15 minutes
 - What are you afraid of?
 - How can you learn to not be afraid?
 - How to look calm even when you're not
 - Concentrating on expression quells nerves

b. Stage presence – 20 minutes
 - Stage attire
 - Using props and equipment
 - Speaking or not speaking
 - Don't make excuses or apologize
 - Smile!
 - Body Language and Mannerisms

c. Making set lists – 10 minutes
 - Make it readable from a distance
 - Include keys and other helpful information

d. How to handle musical mistakes – 15 minutes
 - Playing through errors
 - Improvising around errors
 - Don't let on that you've made a mistake
 - Humor helps

Using Technical Terminology

Be sure you know and use your technical terminology correctly and comfortably. Be able to spell and pronounce all terms correctly. This makes your teaching credible. But beware of using technical terminology to sound like you "know a lot". It is much more kind to your students to use language they already understand than to use technical terms when they aren't necessary. You can explain key words and terms that are important, but constantly using unfamiliar technical terminology can cause eyes to glaze over.

The intelligence of your students should not be underestimated; however, no one is smart enough to understand lingo that they have never heard before. (*Lingo* is a set of terms or a way of speaking used in certain lines of work, by specific groups, or in certain disciplines). *One cannot teach a subject using language that is part of the material to be learned* (just as the dictionary definition of a word never uses the word itself).

Many of us make the mistake of assuming that everyone should already know what we know, and if they don't they are ignorant. This is our own self-esteem issue. Most of us have a tendency to think that the sum total of what we know isn't much beyond what any normal person knows. That is a mistake. Everyone knows different things. Assuming that everyone should already know, for instance, what a bass clef is, would be like believing everyone speaks Sanskrit.

When I was new at my very first job, I learned how prevalent this attitude is. I had been a college-prep student in High School, but found myself working at a lunch counter at Woolworth's. I had no idea how to make fries or how to fill the coke machine. The other employees thought I had no brain whatsoever, and treated me like an idiot. They didn't remember that at one time they had to learn those things, too. The pain of that experience has led me to be very careful to never treat my music students that way.

Podiums and Desks

A good policy regarding about podiums and desks is: *if possible, don't use them*. Body language is important, and standing behind something says you are setting yourself apart, or are intimidated by, the students. Being out in the open says that you are confident and approachable.

One of the best professional speakers I've seen stands *beside* the podium. Once in a while he walks behind it and on to the other side, glancing at his outline on the way by. In this way, you don't get a sense that he's reading from his outline, but speaking directly to his audience.

I sometimes put my outline on the floor in front of me. I always make sure the print is large enough to see from a distance. If it's more than one page long, I might put it on a chair or low table beside me. If I have to pick it up and take a moment to find my place once in a while, that's not a problem. Students understand that teachers need to refer to their outlines.

Whether to stand or sit while teaching a class should be carefully considered. If the class is small, standing to teach can be too formal. For small groups, arranging the chairs in a circle and sitting in the circle as an equal is a good way to put your students at ease. For large groups, standing is best, as it focuses attention, makes you easier to see, and because you can walk around and use body language to make the presentation dynamic.

Do You Know How You Come Across?

One of the most eye-opening things any teacher can do is record yourself speaking in public and then listen to how you sound, and also to video yourself presenting, so you can see and assess your body language. Be prepared for a shock. We all have mannerisms and habits no one tells us about, our voices sound different from what we expect, and our facial expressions may not look like we expect them to. A video assessment can help you realize why people react to you the way they do, be it positive or negative.

There are many teachers and presenters who, if they knew how they appeared, would change their mannerisms. Some have dull, monotone voices; some have annoying speech or physical habits, some dress sloppily, some wear badly done makeup, and so on. Although students ideally should be able to see beyond all that, the fact is they are human, and these things can detract from the quality of a class. So, do yourself a favor and get someone to video your next presentation.

Power Point and Other Visual Aids

Most of us have seen the computer-based visual aid tool called Power Point, which puts images from your computer onto a screen as a slide show that you control. This tool, like any other, is wonderful when used well, and terrible when used poorly. The best use of Power Point is to *illustrate* but not to *reiterate* what is being said. I have *seen* presenters' talks, rather than *heard* them, much too often. I'd rather give my attention to the speaker than to the screen.

Naturally, blackboards and flip charts are still a mainstay of good teaching. If your penmanship is legible, use them to illustrate, clarify, and support what you say.

Anything that you can use to make a class more interesting should certainly be used, if it actually does add to, rather than detract from, your presentation.

"Coyote Teaching"

Have you ever noticed that many people think that if they know *about* something, they know it? Have you ever experienced the difference between reading a cookbook and the reality of what really can happen in your kitchen? How can people actually absorb something, rather than just intellectualize it, if not experiencing it while learning?

Among the wise teachers in American Indian traditions, there is a style of teaching referred to as *Coyote Teaching.* Coyote is clever, and one does not always understand his actions until one sees the results. Coyote Teaching means leading the student to learn through their own innate wisdom, bringing that which is intuitively known to the forefront of their awareness to be recognized, so that learning can take place easily.

I once attended a workshop with Jon Young, a master naturalist who runs the famous Wilderness Awareness School in Washington State. He took our group to a field on the edge of a woodland, instructed us to listen quietly, and asked us what we heard. "A bird", said one man. "What is the bird saying?" asked Jon. "He sounds agitated", said the man. "Yes. Why?" asked Jon. "Because we are here", guessed the man; and as Jon's questions went on, we realized that the bird was warning other birds and animals of our presence. Jon could have told us that, but instead he *asked* us. He asked us a lot of questions that day, and as a result, we learned a great deal, and it was easy, exciting, and not at all a lecture.

Jon could have put us in a classroom and just told us what he knew. But he made it real for us by making us think, by putting us in the environment, by letting us have successes right from the first minute of our class. He is a Coyote Teacher.

How does one teach by asking? We don't need to ask trick questions or begin with esoterica that no one has a clue about. We can, however, ask questions that lead the student or the class into the subject material in a thoughtful way. Let's say you are teaching, for example, music theory. I like to start by saying there are no wrong answers, and asking, "What is music?" After a bit of gently guided discussion, classes usually decide it is a combination of tones with specific pitches. Through that process, they get to discuss what tones and pitches are, and whether or not the combination must contain rhythm, melody, and harmony. Then we move on until we have covered all of basic theory. I always have them *do* on their instruments whatever we talk about. Through continual discussion and application, they see all the relationships and aspects of music theory. It's great to see the lights turn on, the "Aha" happen again and again. And they *never* forget their theory.

So… in addition to the five ways of learning discussed earlier in this chapter (aural, verbal, tactile, experiential, and visual), students learn well in three additional ways:

- By being asked
- By experiencing
- By discussing

What Are Handouts Really For?

Students deserve and expect to take something home from a class or workshop that represents the gist of its content, or perhaps further details of the material covered. The handouts you provide can help the learning process.

Be sure you know in advance how many students you'll have in a class so you can arrive with enough handouts. If you cannot get this information in advance, be sure you have a copy machine or a computer and printer handy.

A handout should:

- Be easy to read
- Remind the student of the content of the class
- Make sense by itself

A handout should *not* be:

- Anything that can't be understood on its own
- A word-for-word printout of a lecture
- Your class outline

I've received handouts that were simply an outline of the class, and made no sense at all because they contained no actual information. On the other hand, I've received some that were so detailed they made the teacher's presentation unnecessary. The best handouts are ones that add to, illustrate, or clarify what you have taught.

If, for instance, I am teaching about ergonomics for musicians, I might wish to hand out pictures of anatomical structure, posture, and some articles others have written on the subject. If I am covering a very involved concept of some kind, I might hand out a document that contains definitions of pertinent terminology or concepts.

However, I almost never hand out something that takes the place of taking notes. If a student does not take notes, no handout can make up for what they should have put in their own language. One learns better from one's own notes than from a reiterative document.

On the other hand, some students take notes as a substitute for learning the material - they keep their brains on paper. If you sense that this is going on, tell them that you prefer that they simply absorb the information.

Varied Skills in the Classroom

Every teacher will run into the joy and challenge of having varied skill levels among a group of students. A class may consist of a few beginners, a few professionals, and several intermediates, for instance. We need to be prepared for this, and we need to treat all students equitably. No one has less or more value than another because of their skill level. Some students may expect preferential treatment, and we must resist offering it, while at the same time being sure we ignore no one.

Here are some guidelines:

- All students have an equal right to participate in class activity, discussion, and music-making, regardless of skill level
- Good teachers are always neutral and do not show favoritism
- Shy students need to be encouraged to participate
- Aggressive students need to be quieted to allow others an equal chance at learning

Respecting a Difficult Student

Occasionally, you will run into a student who is difficult in some way. There are many kinds and levels of possible difficulty, ranging from inattention to disruption of an entire class.

Resistance and Disagreement:

Questioning can be healthy, and it facilitates learning. Every student has a right to question you, but how they do that can be either appropriate or inappropriate.

If someone politely presents another point of view, acknowledge them kindly. I've seen teachers argue with or speak angrily to students when it was not at all necessary to do so.

However, it can be a problem when a student loudly, rudely, or continually disagrees with you. In extreme cases disrespect can simply be handled by asking the student to leave. No one in a class wants to be prevented from learning, and they will be grateful to you for ejecting the offender.

It can be much worse when someone who disagrees with you tells the other students so during class breaks instead of confronting you openly. When this occurs, you can usually tell something is going on. Students' enthusiasm might suddenly lessen or they might look agitated. In that case, you might ask, "How does everyone feel about the material being presented?" That's an invitation for students to ask challenging questions openly. It's an opportunity for discussion, which almost always makes students feel included and respected.

Students Who Don't Speak Up vs. Excessive Talkers:

Once in a while you'll encounter students who don't ask questions or participate. Such students need to be encouraged and included. It's your job to see that students are drawn into participation - even those who never raise their hands.

On the other hand, there is such a thing as "sharing too much", which occurs when a student is overly assertive and verbal. When you have such a student in a class or workshop, you can simply ask everyone not to speak out without raising their hands and being called upon. That way, everyone gets an equal chance. This may seem silly for a room full of adult students, but occasionally some adults do act like undisciplined children! Making this rule is a kindness to the rest of the class.

Pacing the Day

If you're teaching a group in a day-long workshop or class, groups have the most energy and learn best during morning hours. Offer your most intense material in the morning. After lunch, people get sleepy or less attentive. Early afternoon is a good time for an hour or two of interaction and activity, followed by a coffee break. After the break, a review or other simple information will round out the day.

A Student's Responsibilities Are:

- To arrive on time and stay until the lesson or class is over
- To be attentive
- To respect the teacher and the material being presented, and consider the efficacy of the material offered
- To do all the work as requested, and to practice at home between lessons or classes
- To treat other students with respect
- To participate, not just observe
- To wear no perfumes or heavily scented products to lessons or classes
- To speak up politely and respectfully when clarification is needed

A Student's Bill of Rights

- All students are created equal
- All students have a right to retain their own political, religious and spiritual beliefs
- All students pay the same for equal training
- All students have a right to question the teacher or material, pleasantly
- Every student has a right to be encouraged and not unnecessarily criticized

A Teacher's Bill of Rights

- Every teacher deserves respect (but not subservience)
- Every teacher is human and has a right to make human errors, within reason
- Every teacher has a right to reject a student who impedes their ability to teach or interferes with other students' ability to learn
- Every teacher has a right to a classroom free of heavy perfumes and/or odors
- Every teacher has a right to the full attention of every student, within reason

Guidelines to Teach By

- Smile!
- Require no more and no less of each student than they are capable of reasonably doing, accomplishing, or learning.
- Provide breaks, rests, and opportunities for refreshment regularly.
- Foster students' respect for each other.
- Present all available viewpoints on the subject material, not just that which matches your opinions.
- Provide information for further study and additional sources of the subject material.
- Show respect for, and encouragement to, every student.
- Think of yourself less as a disseminator, and more as a facilitator, of learning.
- Bring out the creative spark in each student.
- All students have within them the ability to which they aspire. Show them their capability.
- People enjoy good leadership. Be a confident leader.
- A sense of humor is essential.
- People remember best what they have discovered themselves. They remember least what they have merely been told. Make learning experiential and interactive. Discussion, questions, participation, and activity are all part of learning.
- Recognize, acknowledge and honor individuality.
- Each student learns differently. Flexibility and creativity are a teacher's best tools.
- A good teacher learns from teaching. If you knew all there is to know, there would be little reason to teach.
- When the student's skill surpasses that of the teacher, it's a great day for the teacher.

The Musician's Body

This section covers a variety of physical considerations for all musicians. (Harpists should see my book *The Harper's Manual*[4] for greater and more specific detail relating to playing the harp.)

Ergonomics

To be the best musicians we can be, we need to be sure that how we use our bodies gives us the best results musically. We often don't realize how important ergonomics can be, and may have little awareness of our own bodies as we play. Ideally, good ergonomics should be part of music lessons from the very first, but too often this is not addressed, leaving the musician to assume that discomfort is part of playing.

Neutral posture is a natural, easy, healthy way of standing, sitting, and moving, in which no particular group of muscles works harder than any others to hold you upright. Neutral posture is the foundational position to which we keep returning as we move with our music. It does not need to be held stiffly.

<u>When seated:</u> Neutral posture for playing an instrument or singing is achieved by sitting toward the front edge of a normal dining-room-type chair that has no slope to the seat. Your feet should be directly under your knees, heels on the floor. The sternum should be raised comfortably to achieve a *pleasant* stretching sensation between it and the lumbar region of the back, but the pelvis should *not* be tipped forward. There should be no curve in the lower back. The shoulders should be relaxed but not slumped. The chin should be slightly up, and the head should not tilt.

<u>When standing:</u> Neutral posture aligns the top of the head to the joints where the toes meet the foot, in a straight plumb line. It will feel as though you are about to start walking, because your balance is forward. The heels should be firmly on the floor, and

the pelvis neither forced forward nor slumping backward. The sternum should be raised comfortably. The shoulders should be relaxed but not slumped. The chin should be forward and up. Knees should be loose, not locked. Feet should point forward, about twelve inches apart.

It is to neutral posture, standing or sitting, that the musical instrument should be adjusted, *even if it compromises the "correct" way of holding the instrument.* (If the "correct way" injures the body, how correct can it be?)

Technique Issues for Instrumentalists

Many of us have been taught techniques which, regardless of their credibility, have contributed to injury. We have worked hard to perfect those techniques, have been lectured on why we must use them, and have developed a big investment in having those techniques be right. But what may be right for one person may injure another. There is more than one correct way use the arms, hands, and fingers.

A common technique-related injury is *repetitive motion syndrome*, which in actuality should be called *repetitive-motion-under-stress syndrome*. Tendons, which connect bones to muscles and are responsible for movement, must be treated with care when repetitive movement is involved. Repetitive motion itself is not bad as long as the tendons and muscles are not under stress.

For instance, think of the tender filet mignon. This cut of meat comes from the muscles that wag the tail of the cow. Cows spend their whole lives moving their tails back and forth, and yet this muscle is so soft that it makes the most tender cut of meat. This is because the cow habitually lets its tail dangle easily from its body, so there is no stress to the muscles that move the tail. If, however, the cow were to make a habit of holding its tail stiffly and wagging it, the stressed muscles would overdevelop and lose their elasticity; the filet mignon would be tough indeed.

Look at the difference between a body-builder and a yogi. The bodybuilder spends his time contracting his muscles under stress. His muscles are very hard and overdeveloped, and cannot stretch. The yogi both flexes and stretches his muscles, and never under stress. His muscles are very elastic, and he or she is agile yet quite strong.

Because many musicians use tense techniques, pain or stiffness in the hands is a common problem. Your playing technique should be a relaxed one that does not involve tensing the muscles that move repetitively. Stiff fingers, hands, wrists, or arms promote injury.

When we move our fingers, the tendons responsible are not just in the fingers. Finger movement is governed by tendons that begin at the fingers but travel through the hand and wrist, and become muscles in the forearm. Therefore, finger movement originates in the forearm. If you are holding any part of the arm, wrist, or hand awkwardly or stiffly, the tendons leading to the fingers can be affected. Conversely, if you have pain in the arm, it can originate from awkward finger movement.

Keep track of what you do with your hands in your everyday activities. If, in addition to playing an instrument, you use tools of any kind, or work with your hands in other ways, be careful with them. Computer users and gardeners, for instance, typically have a high rate of chronic injury.

If you talk on the phone for more than about 15 minutes a day, holding the receiver to your ear can stiffen and injure the hand or wrist. (Your neck can develop problems, too, from tilting your head as you use the phone.) Get a headset for your phone and free your hands.

Texting on a cell phone is especially bad for the muscles of the hand and can lead to permanent injury when over-used.

If you have already injured your hand(s) or arm(s), no matter how you did it, stop using the injured hand or arm. If your injury was caused by the way you play your instrument, you must change the way you play so that you will not keep injuring yourself.

One more factor in keeping your hands and wrists healthy: think about how you hold your hands when they are not in use. Is there any tension held in them, do you keep your fingers stiff or do you clench your fists? Be aware, and learn to keep them relaxed.

When a muscle or tendon has been suddenly strained and is swollen, hot, and/or the surrounding tissue is red, using ice is a common treatment to reduce swelling. However, when the injury has come on slowly and there is no obvious inflammation, ice can actually make it worse; try dry heat, such as a heating pad. This can relax the injured tendon or muscle and increase circulation to the area.

Pain relievers are often recommended for conditions like tendonitis, carpal tunnel syndrome, tenosynovitis, and other repetitive motion injuries. They mask the pain, but let's look at pain from another perspective. Pain is a warning that something is wrong, and its purpose is to prevent you from using the affected area further. The body has its own wisdom! Masking pain merely allows you to keep using, and therefore to further damage, the injured area.

If you have a repetitive motion injury, seek treatment immediately with a musicians' therapist (not a sports therapist - that's a very different treatment philosophy).

Occupational Therapists can be helpful, but remember they are human and can only help you as much as is humanly possible. The rest is up to you; you must be totally committed to overcoming the injury. (When surgery is suggested, be sure to get a second opinion.) And once the problem heals, never use again the same position, technique, or stressful motion that injured you in the first place - retrain yourself to use a new, non-injurious technique.

This is only the beginning of the information you need, and it takes more than a chapter of one book to address it. There is an excellent book and DVD on ergonomics by Julie Lyon Lieberman[3] called *You Are Your Instrument.* Taking classes in Alexander Technique[5] or another postural re-education system can also be enormously helpful.

The information on injury in this chapter is not given for the purpose of self-diagnosis, is not an official prescription, and is not meant to replace a consultation with your doctor; rather it is to make a point: discomfort and injury are serious issues and must be prevented and treated responsibly. We can permanently lose our ability to play our instruments if we don't respond to the warning signs that tell us when we are doing something unwise with our bodies.

Breathing

Breathing should be practiced into your pieces. When you begin to play a piece, consciously relax and breathe smoothly and deeply while you play. Remember to do this on stage as well as at home. You will find that not only does your body feel more alive, but your music suddenly begins to flow and sound alive too.

It is helpful to know that breathing not only brings oxygen into the body, giving our muscles the ability to move (as well as enhancing all our body functions), but that breathing also speeds the process of elimination of toxic by-products from our muscles every time we exhale. If we do not breathe regularly and deeply, our muscles, laden with lactic acid and other toxins, will not function properly. (Excess lactic acid can cause soreness in muscle tissue. Sometimes taking several deep breaths will eliminate pain immediately with no other effort involved!)

Physical Health

Making music professionally or as a serious avocation requires physical effort and mental concentration, which in turn require good over-all health. Good health is promoted through good diet, exercise, plenty of rest and relaxation, avoidance of stress, and moderation in all things. Let's look at each of these:

Diet

You may ask, *how on earth does anything we eat affect our music?* But some of the simplest answers are well known: for instance, a singer avoids dairy products before singing because dairy products encourage mucus production. Caffeine makes us jittery, so most instrumentalists avoid caffeine before playing because it makes our playing less accurate and too fast. Alcohol dulls the senses and judgment, so it's wise not to drink before a performance. These are obvious things.

However, there are also many subtle effects of diet on our ability to play or sing well. Anything that affects our health affects our music.

In the previous section we discussed musicians' injuries. Some of these injuries are exacerbated by dietary factors. Repetitive motion injuries are more common than ever before. Have you ever wondered why? What's different now? Instruments haven't changed much. Other repetitive motions like knitting have not changed, and typing has become easier with computers instead of old-fashioned typewriters. If repetitive motion were so bad for us, activities humans have been doing since the dawn of time would not have been so popular, like carving, sewing by hand, grinding grain, shelling peas, husking corn, and so on.

What has changed is our diet. We now eat far less of the things that keep our muscles, tendons, and joints healthy, and a lot more of the things that don't.

In addition to the proper amounts of minerals, vitamins, proteins, and fiber in our diets, there are two kinds of substances that are essential for joint and muscle health: sticky fats and lubricating fats. ("Fats" have been maligned in popular diet lingo, but what we're not usually told is that only certain kinds of fats which, in certain quantities, are culprits. Others are absolutely essential to life.) Simply said, sticky fats hold the tissues together, while lubricating fats allow smooth movement of tissues such as muscles and joints.

Both sticky fats and lubricating fats used to be present in the human diet in balanced amounts. Now it is almost exclusively the sticky fats that that are used in processed foods. In popular terms, these are the cholesterol-based fats.

The lubricating fats are called Essential Fatty Acids (EFA's), because we cannot live without them. They are important in many vital functions. The two important EFA's are Linoleic and Linolenic Acid, and these are the ones that are seriously lacking in the modern diet. They are easily destroyed by light, heat, and air, so they are not present in most of the foods we buy. They should be present in fresh seeds, nuts and grains, but because these are usually stored for long periods of time after harvest, the EFA's in them are degraded and useless. Fish such as salmon contain them, but only if not cooked. Cooking destroys EFA's.

Aleuts and Inuits in extreme northern climates used to eat quantities of raw fish and sea mammal blubber, which is rich in EFA's. They were very healthy people until they adopted the typical modern American way of eating. Now they suffer from a high rate of heart disease.

Interestingly, in tropical climates naturally-occurring foods contain fewer EFA's. This is because sunshine has an effect on the body similar to EFA's, making them less necessary in the diets of tropical dwellers.

Many of us are aware of a condition called Seasonal Affective Disorder (SAD), in which those living in northern climates (where it is dark in the winter) are prone to depression. How come the Inuits and Aleuts didn't have this problem historically? Because their diet was rich in EFA's. Where there is less sunshine, EFA's are crucial. The best treatment for SAD is adding EFA's to our diet. (By the way, Vitamin D3 is also essential, and should be added to the diet as a supplement if you don't spend at least 15 minutes a day in the sun.)

The easiest source of EFA's is organic, raw, whole flax. Usually we're advised to ingest it in the form of flax oil, and many companies promote this product at health food stores. But consider this: to make oil, the flax seeds have to be processed, exposing them to light, heat, and air. Regardless of what the companies claim, much of the essential nutrient in flax oil has been destroyed. And if you heat the oil, or even just don't refrigerate it, that makes it worse. Likewise, flax seed "meal" or powder sold in jars is only minimally beneficial, for the same reasons.

Why not go directly to the source? The whole seeds are *much* less expensive (they literally cost just pennies), and are easy to prepare.

Preparation of flax seeds:

Buy raw, whole, organic seeds. Buy a pound or two, and put them in the freezer immediately. Take out ¼ cup of them and put them in a coffee mill for about one second - only until the seeds are opened, but *not* long enough to turn them into powder. Put the chopped seeds into an airtight, opaque container in your freezer. Every day, eat about ¼ teaspoon of them; sprinkle them on cold cereals and salads or put them in smoothies. Never heat or cook them!

Don't eat them whole - no amount of chewing can open these slippery little seeds sufficiently, and when eaten whole, they merely have a laxative effect.

Exercise

We evolved as hunter-gatherers, and have not yet physically evolved beyond that. Even though our modern lives have us spending our days at computers, watching TV, and so on, our bodies are not ready to be sedentary, evolutionarily speaking. Hunter-gatherers ran, squatted, stretched, climbed, lifted, hurled objects, and did every imaginable kind of physical motion and action, both flexing and stretching muscles constantly. We, too need to do these things regularly, even if only in the gym.

Complete exercise involves *stretching* (as in Yoga or ballet), *flexing* (as in isometrics and weight training), and *movement* (as in aerobics, dancing and running). All three kinds of exercise are necessary; doing only one kind causes an imbalance that can be harmful.

We cannot ignore our bodies and expect to stay healthy. Many of us find our bodies getting stiff and painful, and wonder what disease we might have, when all we may need is some consistent exercise. Exercise is the greatest pain-reliever available to us. It is also the best energizer and the finest treatment for depression. It releases endorphins, brings oxygen to all the body tissues, promotes release and excretion of toxins, promotes heart health, burns excess calories, increases metabolic rate, tunes up the endocrine system, builds strength and endurance, makes the joints and tendons more flexible, and tones the muscles. What else can do all that?

Stress Reduction

Many of us burn our candles at both ends. Musicians especially tend to keep late hours. After being up late for performances, many of us get up early so we won't be labeled "lazy musicians", or we may have "day jobs". We need more rest than we usually get. It's known that in a 90-minute concert, a musician can use as many calories as someone running ten miles. That's not rock musicians, by the way (who do a lot of dancing around on stage), but *classical* musicians. Intense concentration, mental and emotional exertion use more calories than we might realize.

Musicians know that even if we've conquered stage fright, our work is still very stressful. For instance, being a touring musician is akin to being an executive who every day must travel a long distance to a new office, with all new co-workers, a different desk and chair, a different telephone system, a different computer, and different procedures to follow, and still do high quality work!

Stress affects our ability to learn, concentrate, and perform well, it decreases our enjoyment in playing, and it deteriorates our health. How can we deal with stress? A good start is to moderate everything you do: eating, sleeping, practicing, performing, traveling, exercising. Don't allow yourself to be proud of being too busy. Learn to say no. Pace yourself.

Friends of mine found themselves overburdened with their home-based business. They were working seven days a week and still did not have enough hours in each day to get their work done. What did they do? They decided to take two days a week off! Soon they found that in the remaining five days, they were accomplishing more than ever before. It worked because they were refreshed, and therefore more efficient. No one can work all the time and retain maximum efficiency.

Developing a routine is part of stress reduction. Most of us stress, whether we are aware of it or not, over not knowing when something will be done. A routine assures that everything will be done.

On the following page are some sample daily schedules. Find the one with the title that best describes you. If it seems unrealistic to you, look carefully - there are a full 24 hours in the schedule and plenty of time for everything. (If other people in your life demand more of you, ask yourself if they are carrying their fair share of the load.)

Try one of these schedules for at least two weeks. Set a timer for each activity, and when it sounds, *stop* what you are doing and go on to the next activity. After two weeks, make any modifications you need, and continue your new good habits!

Daily Schedule for a Professional Musician Without Children:

Meditate ½ hour
Breakfast ½ hour
Phone calls 1/2 hour
Break 15 minutes
Practice music 1 hour
Break 15 minutes
Desk work 1 hour
Lunch 1/2 hour
Take a walk or do Yoga 1 hour
Nap 1 hour
Desk work 2 hours
Break, snack ½ hour
Dinner 2 hours
Practice 1 hour
E-mail 2 hours
Relax 2 hours (read, watch TV, whatever…)
Sleep 8 hours

Daily Schedule for a Professional Musician With Children

Meditate ½ hour
Breakfast ½ hour
Drive kids to school or do laundry ½ hour
Practice music 1 hour
Phone calls and e-mail 1 hour
Break 15 minutes
Desk work 45 minutes
Lunch ½ hour
Take a walk or do Yoga I hour
Nap 1 hour
Housework 2 hours
Errands and taxiing kids to activities 3 hours
Dinner 2 hours
Relax with Family 2 hours
Sleep 8 hours

Daily Schedule for Amateur Musician with Full-time (unrelated) Job Outside the House

Meditate, exercise, or do Yoga 1/ 2hour
Breakfast ½ hour
Work and commute 10 hours
Dinner 1 hour
Practice music 1 hour
Housework 1 hour
Relax 2 hours (read, watch TV, whatever…)
Sleep 8 hours

Music as Therapy

Beneficial Resonant Frequencies

Every structure, living or nonliving, has a "resonant frequency", also called a resonance point. Very simply put, every structure emits a sound of its own, which defines its structural integrity (ability to hold together) and/or its ability to sustain its function.

Every part and organ of the human body has one, or a set of, resonant frequencies. These are not necessarily in the range of human hearing, but when multiplied or divided by octave factors, they can be expressed as musical tones.

At lower amplitudes, reinforcing resonant frequencies can have a beneficial effect on living things. One can support the body's healthy resonant frequencies by playing tones that are related to those frequencies in audible pitches - this is called harmonic resonance. This principle is used by Music Practitioners, Clinical Musicians, and Harp Therapists in their work with therapeutic applications of music. These professionals undergo rigorous training and are employed in hospitals worldwide.

It should be noted that there is no specific set of frequencies that are therapeutic for everyone. Practitioners learn how to determine the frequencies to which each individual best responds. The variables involved include the person's weight, bone density, gender, age, and ailment, to name just a few.

Although it is not an exact science, locating resonant frequencies (specific tones) is easily done through observation and communication with patients while playing restful, live acoustic music for them at a pleasant volume. Repetition of specific notes that patients can physically feel reverberating through their bodies, when the sensation is pleasant, can be repeated for the patients' benefit. Research has backed up the efficacy of this practice.

Different organs of the body have different frequencies, and disease processes alter those frequencies. Re-establishing healthy frequencies through entrainment can help the body move back toward health.

Aside from tone, frequency can also be expressed in terms of tempo (beats per minute). Remember, "frequency" simply means *a repeating event.* A practitioner can play music in a tempo that mimics the rate of a healthy heartbeat, to encourage entrainment to that rate. Entrainment is simply the tendency of one object's frequency to match a frequency to which it is exposed. Some frequencies are toxic and some support health.

A good example of entrainment occurs in experiments with living chicken heart muscle tissue in laboratories. Heart tissue beats on its own without need of the autonomic nervous system, and therefore, heart tissue kept alive in laboratories will pulsate. When brought into close contact with each other, separate pieces of heart tissue will begin to beat at the same pulse, and continue to do so until separated. Gabor Forgacs, a biophysics researcher at the University of Missouri-Columbia has actually seen separate particles of chicken heart cells fuse and beat in unison in a petrie dish.

Very generally, here are some frequencies (rates of repetition) of human body functions:

- Heart rate for a healthy adult averages 60 to 80 beats per minute (bpm). 60 bpm=1 Hz (1 beat or "cycle" per second)
- Respiration for a healthy adult averages 12-16 breaths per minute.
- Gastric cycle: the stomach contracts on an average of once every 3 minutes.
- Intestinal cycle: the intestines contract in waves about once per minute.

There are also brain wave frequencies. The brain produces alpha, beta, delta, and theta frequencies. Normal frequencies are generally:

- Delta (deepest sleep) = 1 to 3 cps (cycles per second)
- Theta (sleep) = 4 to 8 cps
- Alpha (light slumber) = 9 to 16 cps
- Beta (awake) = 17 to 22 cps

Eminent mathematician Barbara Hero and sound healer researchers Jonathan Goldman and Kay Gardner have each published information the resonant frequencies for each organ and function of the body. When the frequencies given are audible to the human ear, it must be noted that these are the organ frequencies multiplied by octave factors so they can be applied musically. It is also important to know that they are actually approximate. The charts developed by these and other researchers do not necessarily match - this is not an exact science because no two bodies are exactly alike.

Researchers Bruce Tainio and Gary Young have stated that the normal frequency range of the human body is between 62-68 MHz; but if it drops below that, the individual becomes a candidate for illness. Cold symptoms appear at 58 MHz, flu symptoms at 57 MHz, Candida at 55 MHz, Epstein Barr at 52 MHz, and cancer at 42 MHz.

Certain sound healers declare that if we can keep the body's frequency "high enough" we will be free of disease. A great deal more research needs to be done to back up this idea. Meanwhile, we do know that in general, therapeutic music and sound, when carefully and responsibly applied, are beneficial.

Destructive Frequencies

There are some sounds that can cause harm. For instance, crystal bowls, which are popular meditation tools, produce a fairly pure and very loud tone that has been known to cause migraines and even seizures in some people. In therapeutic situations, using just any tone-producing instrument without knowing much about its actual effects is never a good idea.

Tonal frequencies at very high amplitudes and/or extremely high pitches can be quite negative; structural integrity can be destroyed, because the high amplitude and/or high pitch sets up a feedback loop that exponentially increases volume to a destructive level.

(What is a feedback loop? An example is when a "live" microphone faces a speaker, causing a spontaneous loud hum that raises in pitch and volume to the point of pain, and sends everyone scurrying to turn the speaker and microphone away from each other. The microphone picks up sound, the speaker broadcasts the sound back into the microphone, which further amplifies it and feeds it back to the speaker, in an endless loop called feedback.)

A good example of destructive power of very high amplitude is deafness caused by exposure to high-decibel music or other loud sounds such as explosions.

Destruction of matter using very high pitches or very loud amplitude is done most easily with rigid forms and less easily with flexible or soft forms. For instance, ultrasound is commonly used to break down scar tissue, which is more rigid than healthy tissue.

Cymatics - Visible Effects of Frequency on Matter

Researcher Hans Jenny proved that sound causes movement in matter. This phenomenon has been named *Cymatics*[12]. Dynamic shapes are formed from matter exposed to specific tones. Matter is prone to inertia (unmoving) until activated by these tones (frequencies). Certain powders and liquids, when influenced by specific frequencies, form complex geometric patterns resembling mandalas, crystal structures, cell structures, living creatures, fish skeletons, solar systems, cells, plants, and so on; all moving, undulating, and rotating within themselves. One of my favorites is an organic-looking shape that forms in lycopodium powder (fern pollen), which actually *crawls* across surfaces, and resembles in almost perfect detail a prehistoric aquatic creature called a trilobite. The footage can be seen on the DVD cited in endnote 12. Because the science of Cymatics is so thoroughly covered in books and DVD's that are readily available, I will not reiterate here. Please see the recommended materials.

Entrainment

Although our own bodies produce many frequencies of sound, we don't hear most of them, because if we did, we would be unable to distinguish sounds outside of us from sounds inside of us. Our neurologic system is set up to ignore constantly occurring internal sounds.

Likewise, sounds outside of us that are the same frequency as our own sounds are not particularly noticeable to us. And sounds that we hear constantly become part of our own frequency, so we cease to notice them as well. We *entrain* to those frequencies. We become those sounds and they become us.

Except in cases where music is purposely used therapeutically, people tend to listen to whatever type of music contains tempos, rhythms, and pitches with frequencies most closely matching their own. An obvious example is the music teenagers prefer, which irks their parents because it is so different from the frequencies that are close to the parents' own. Teens are full of nervous energy, and, generally speaking, so is their music.

Music can be used to enhance an existing state of mind, or to change it. Studies in which teens in controlled environments were consistently exposed to music that imperceptibly changed over a period of weeks to more therapeutic tones, rhythms and tempos showed that the teens didn't notice the changes, but that their behavior changed along with it. (More detail on similar and related studies can be found in *The Power of Sound* by Joshua Leeds[20], published by Healing Arts Press.)

When would it be beneficial to enhance one's mood or behavior, and when is it a good idea to change them, using music? If the mood or behavior is harmful in any way, changing it gently with music can be good therapy. But in some cases, music can be used for catharsis. When feeling sad, for instance, "sad" music can have a cathartic effect that helps us move through our sadness more easily. At first it may evoke tears, but the usual subsequent outcome is relief.

Sound Pollution

Just as exposure to pleasant, therapeutic sound results in better health, consistent exposure to unpleasant and stressful sounds creates stressed people, through entrainment. Unpleasant sound, especially when it is consistently occurring, is called *sound pollution*. We may not always be able to avoid sound pollution.

How can we get back into balance after or during exposure to it? The easiest method is to listen to pleasant, restful music; even quiet music can drown out street noise and most mechanical noise.

Getting outdoors into nature is as helpful as music is; there is therapeutic sound in nature. A rushing stream, birds singing, bees humming, trees rustling in the breeze; *these are the natural sounds with which the human race evolved, and to which we are attuned.* We have not yet evolved into beings who respond well physically to mechanical and electronic sounds.

What happens in noisy hospitals where sick people are trying to get well? Especially in intensive care units, sounds can be unpleasant and not conducive to the life-saving efforts of the care teams. Monitors beep and buzz, respirators whoosh and click. Urgent voices abound. In these settings, restful music can be a welcome intervention and defense against sound pollution.

Types of Therapeutic Music

Here is a list of the basic uses and types of therapeutic music:

1. *Service* (passive therapy): live music at the bedside of inpatients as unobtrusive enhancement to the healing environment; does not require active listening, and solicitation of a response or interaction is not appropriate. Those qualified to do this work are Music Practitioners, Certified Clinical Musicians, Certified Harp Thanatologists, Certified Harp Therapists, Certified healing Musicians, and Certified Bedside Harpists.

2. *Recorded music:* used for individual patients: this can be any type of music used for a variety of reasons, such as therapy or entertainment.

3. *Entertainment*: music played or sung, live or recorded, in a common area or day room where patients may come for entertainment. All of the above certified musicians are qualified to do this work, as well as Music Therapists. In

some cases, non-certified musicians can entertain in waiting rooms and lobbies.

4. *Interactive Therapy*: live or recorded music used with groups or individuals in medical or behavioral-health settings for the purpose of social or neurologic therapy/rehabilitation. Those qualified to do this work are Music Therapists.

5. *Self-directed Sound Healing:* self-directed live music and sound are used by an individual for personal benefit; methods may include toning, chanting, playing an instrument, and/or singing. Anyone may use music privately for their own purposes.

6. *Other-Directed Sound Healing*: live or recorded music and sound for another person's benefit or for a group, not in medical settings; may include toning, chanting, playing an instrument, and/or singing. These may also be used as an adjunct to Guided Imagery, meditation, Reiki, massage, etc. Musicians who work in this capacity should be trained specifically in Sound Healing.

The Wholistic Continuum

Our responses to music occur throughout the entire the mind-body system. We respond physically, emotionally, mentally, and spiritually. Ancient cultures around the world have held a more than coincidental and very detailed understanding of the relationship of music, medicine, art, philosophy, technology, and spiritual life. All the mythologies and cosmologies of the world reflect this. In the modern world we separate these things. It would behoove is to put them back together - the puzzle is not complete otherwise.

We've been caught in an illusion that the mind and the body are separate - that which dwells inside the skull, and that which is the rest of us. Culturally, we've gone so far with this idea that we tend to think of the body as merely a vehicle for the mind. We even view portraits of faces as though they were the whole person. A keen observer, however, knows that the story of one's life is told in the body - how we move, how we hold it, how we use it.

We also tend to think of *brain* and *mind* as the same thing. But in truth the brain does not contain the entirety of the mind. Interestingly, information from sensory perception has been shown to cause simultaneous reaction throughout the body, even though it was formerly thought that information had to travel to the brain first and then be sent to whatever parts of the body needed to react. But not only has this been disproven, but it has also been seen that at times the body reacts *before* the brain receives the information! (See Candace Pert[7] and Margo Drohan[21])

In the past few decades, we have moved into a new paradigm in which it is accepted that the mind and the body are integrated. Hence the term *Mind-Body.*

It is important, however, to be aware that the integration of mind and body must be seen from many angles. When the body reacts to sensory input, that's physical. It behooves us to see this as brain-body being integration. When the body reacts by producing "molecules of emotion"[7] or holding unexpressed emotions in the cells, this is *mind*-body integration. It's easy to see that there is such a fine line between the functions of brain, body, and mind, to the degree that they are not distinguishable in some cases. But distinguish we must, for although our bodies are indeed vehicles and do express who we are on very deep levels, *we are not our bodies.*

When a person stands at the grave of a loved one, saying they are "visiting" that person, who are they visiting? Physically, they're visiting a plot of ground within which lies the decaying frame of what used to be a vehicle for a person. But the person is no longer there. Where did the person go?

I can only begin to answer this question by telling my own story. After having a busy career as a touring musician, pioneer in therapeutic music, speaker and teacher, I became ill and was in bed for nearly two years. For months I was unable to do anything; even turning my head was excruciating. At times I couldn't think, remember the names of friends who visited me, or carry on a conversation, and my memory faded. During this time it became clear to me that who I was had nothing to do with my body. My essence was unchanged when my body failed to do its job properly; the body is just *one* expression of the Self.

If we identify with our bodies - if we think they contain the sum of who we are - I think we short-change ourselves. I don't claim to have healed myself; such things are far more complex. But knowing that my deepest essence was not affected by the antics of my body is, I believe, a large part of what allowed my body to eventually move back toward physical health.

A dear elderly friend of mine fell and broke her hip, wrist and shoulder when she was 91. One might have expected her to decline rapidly after such a trauma. Instead, she put her mind to recovery, and decline was never part of her belief system. She regained use of all her limbs, and in a year's time was in better health than she had been before her fall. This was an excellent example of how attitude and state of mind can affect the outcome of a challenging physical situation. It's not that she wasn't prone to discouragement from time to time, but overall, she maintained a positive outlook and the results followed.

Some would go so far as to say that illness originates in the mind. Taken to the extreme, this philosophy can promote the idea that we cause illness subconsciously. But look at how imperfect the body is even in the best of health! If one believes that perfection is possible, then the fact that one has a body is in itself proof that one is still far from attaining perfection! Seeing a person who is sick as inferior is misplaced thinking, and negates the possibility of compassion.

Even spiritual masters die; Ramana Maharshi died of cancer; Mother Teresa died of heart failure, Teresa of Avila had frail health all her life and died young, the Buddha died of a sudden illness, and so on.

States of mind do not dictate the body's status, but they do *affect* the body, sometimes profoundly. Simple examples are: we sweat and breathe hard when frightened, blush when embarrassed, become nauseated when confronted with visual horror, get "goose bumps" when something awes us, and so on. There is even a physical condition called "Broken Heart Syndrome[22]", also called *stress cardiomyopathy*. Johns Hopkins researchers discovered that emotional shock can trigger sudden surges of stress hormones that weaken the heart and mimic a heart attack. Published in The New England Journal of Medicine online in 2010, the research team found that large amounts of catecholamines (epinephrine and norepinephrine) can cause chest pain, fluid in the lungs, shortness of breath and heart failure. Many of the patients were previously healthy and have few risk factors for heart disease. (See this website:
http://www.hopkinsmedicine.org/press_releases/2005/02_10_05.h tml)

It is also known that negative states of mind inhibit production of endorphins and other hormones that promote healthy immune function, thereby suppressing immune response against communicable diseases and cancer. It has even been shown that there is a higher rate of recovery from heart disease when treated wholistically rather than with just medication, diet and exercise[23].

When treating illness, we must treat the body, mind and spirit, because physical health or illness *affect* the mind and spirit, and - vice versa - states of mind can effect our health. But I caution you to refrain from carrying too far the idea that we can create perfect and permanently healthy bodies by will alone, or that imperfect health is a sign of inferiority.

Psychoneuroimmunology and Audioanalgesia

The field of psychoneuroimmunology[23] describes the effects neuropeptides have on our emotions. When a person is in a relaxed state, beta-endorphins are released, and the body is allowed to do its own healing. The key here is "relaxed state", meaning freedom from the interference of stressors and interruption. Stressors can be states of mind such as worry, grief, too much responsibility, and so on, or they can be external such as aural or visual input. Achieving freedom from stressors can be as simple as sitting quietly, or as complex as changing one's life.

Psycho (mind)- neuro (nerve or neuron)- immunology (resistance to disease) is an interesting word which I feel expresses a somewhat limited viewpoint of the phenomenon of neuropeptide activity. It assumes that nerve or brain cells are affected by the mind, when relaxed, to produce immunologic response. But there is so much more than that! *All* our cells and systems are affected by deeper states of consciousness brought on by relaxation.

When a relaxed state in which pain is relieved is brought on by listening to music, the result is called *audioanalgesia.* "Audio" means hearing, and "analgesia" means relief from pain. It is one of the most commonly documented responses to therapeutic music. Audioanalgesia and psychoneuroimmunology can go hand in hand as a result of appropriately and skillfully applied therapeutic music.

Margo Drohan[21] wrote an excellent paper on the subject of psychoneuroimmunology and audioanallgesia, called *From Myth to reality - Music's Role in Healing.* I highly recommend reading this document.

Effects of Toning and Chant

Of the two vocal forms called *Toning* and *Chant*, the more commonly known to the general public is chant. Chants from the Middle Ages in Christian Europe, and from Tibet, India and Africa, have become fairly popular in the Western world.

Chant usually involves the use of words, phrases, or word-like sounds. The formation of different vowel sounds causes certain overtones to resonate within the body. Experienced toners and chanters can readily hear and/or feel these overtone frequencies.

The formation of consonant sounds in chanting has a rhythmic effect. This, too, creates beneficial frequency.

Many chants use the vocal range of the chanter much like singing, and sound quite musical. Some forms of chanting, such as that from Tibet, is less musical in nature. Each has its own purpose.

The fact that many of the chant traditions are religious in nature is not coincidental. The physical and psychological benefits can hardly be separated from the spiritual benefits of chant, as each supports the other. Chant is both Wholistic and Holistic.

Toning resembles chant, but without the use of words or syllables. Researcher-neurophysiologist Dr. Ranjie Singh[24] has done over 300 studies of melatonin production and regulation related to toning. In these studies, toning is a self-therapeutic activity, though in practice it can also be used as an interactive or passive therapy.

Both chanting and toning consist of producing long musical tones, often deep, and the pitch can vary. A full spectrum of pitch is most effective; hence the benefit of producing *overtones*. (Overtone chanting is a technique wherein one produces more than one note at the same time; the primary note is enhanced by the simultaneous sound of one or more sympathetic harmonizing notes that change as the primary note changes.)

Many who are reluctant to tone say they cannot do it because they don't sing well. But in toning one is not seeking to make the sound acceptable to a listening audience. Singing usually doesn't produce a full range of vocal sound, whereas toning can. Toning is not always pretty, nor should it be. However, the exercise given the vocal cords in toning can improve the singing voice.

Both toning and chanting are most effectively done with all upper-body cavities - sinuses, nose, mouth, soft palate, throat, trachea, and lungs - held open so they can enhance vibration, just as the sounding chamber of any musical instrument does; the body is, after all, a musical instrument.

The frequencies of different vowel sounds at different pitches can be felt in specific areas of the body. A low "ah" sound is usually felt as vibration in the lower abdomen; "ooh" is usually felt in the upper abdomen; "ay" is usually felt in the chest; and "ee" is usually felt in the lower skull. A hard "eey" (with the y being pronounced as the in the word *yes*) is usually felt at the top of the skull. Not coincidentally, this progression of sounds, if starting at the top with "eey" and moving directly to the bottom with "ah" and then upward through the vowels (eey-ah-ooh-ay-ee) produces a word better known as YAHWEH, which we know as the Hebrew word for the full circle, the Complete, the Divine (though many other cultures use some version of the same word).

Chants from India may use a *Mantra*, a simple word from the ancient Sanskrit language that is repeated, or may contain longer Sanskrit or Hindi phrases that repeat. The syllable OM or AUM, for instance, is considered a mantra, and when pronounced carefully, sets up pleasant vibrations within the resonant chambers of the chest and head, and can be felt throughout the body. For the authors of the ancient Vedic scriptures of the Upanishads, the syllable AUM represented Brahman, the Divine, as well as the whole of creation.

In toning, the sounds produced can touch the psyche in unexpected ways. A common occurrence is a sudden rush of emotion and, as a result, a cathartic array of sounds can well up and be expressed. These sounds are usually not musical, but they seem to relieve and even heal whatever has been held inside.

Holding-in of emotion and lack of expression have been shown to contribute to impaired immune response and susceptibility to pathogenic states. By contrast, in cultures where active, noisy mourning is permissible and encouraged when someone dies, the length of time it takes to move through the stages of grief[25] is shortened considerably. It is possible that in the United States, our stoic way of mourning actually prolongs the grief process. Freely making sounds that express our emotions is profoundly cathartic and beneficial.

More information on toning and chanting can be found in the works of John Beaulieu[26] and Jonathan Goldman[16].

Many Healing Modalities

Since the 1970's, a number of healing modalities have come into use quite prominently and have become nearly as popular in our culture as allopathic medicine. Now, the western-medicine (allopathic) community is beginning to embrace them. These were at first called "alternative" modalities, because they represented something different from mainstream western medicine. Now, healing modalities that are not allopathic are usually called "complementary" modalities.

Many of these modalities have been used since ancient times and are in fact so old that their beginnings fade into prehistory. Why would they have been used so consistently for eons? *Because they work.* If they didn't, people would have stopped using them long ago.

On the other hand, some of these modalities are no longer applicable in the modern world because our cultural paradigms have changed. And even some newer modalities have not proven their effectiveness in practicum. Since there is no overseeing quality-control entity, each of us must judge these healing methods for ourselves.

In Larry Dossey's book *Healing Words*[27], which is an exploration of the effects of prayer and intention, Dossey introduces the concept of three points of view in healing modalities:

1. that which takes a mechanical/physical approach;
2. that which takes a bodymind approach where mind is synonymous with brain and integration is implied;
3. that which takes a nonphysical approach, where "mind" includes and implies a connection with others and/or with a higher consciousness or source.

Is it possible that the mind is bigger than the individual? Can there be a direct connection with others, and if so, how many others? Dr. Dossey discusses this in detail, citing research that certainly can lead us to look at the possibility that we are all part of a *community of mind.*

I would like to take this idea a step further, referring to the above approaches as Paradigms 1, 2 and 3, and apply them to specific healing arts. In the following chart of Healing Modalities, you will see a number 1, 2 or 3 after each one listed, indicating which paradigm the modality fits into.

I would like to point out that I make a distinction between *Holistic* and *Wholistic* in describing certain modalities. They are different words and should not be used interchangeably. *Wholistic* refers to viewing something from a whole perspective, a broad one, looking at all the possible factors and influences involved. *Holistic* comes from *holy*, referring to the use, recognition, or guidance of a higher source. Hence the list below has separate categories for each of these. There are modalities that address only the physical, or only the spiritual, or only the psychological; therefore a wholistic approach - a combination of them - can be most effective.

Below is a list of healing modalities. It was originally put together by Rebecca L. Lieser, MD. I have expanded it. The purpose of its inclusion here is to see where among them therapeutic music stands.

Please note that the simple definitions for each modality in the following chart are not meant to be a complete or official description of the modality, and also that their inclusion in this book does not indicate any recommendation to forego mainstream medical care. Also, the listing of a modality in this chart does not necessarily signify its validity.

Keep in mind when looking at the symbols for the historical age of each modality that most were prevalent only in certain cultures, which may not necessarily have been European.

HEALING MODALITIES CHART

Key to symbols:

* requires a degree, certification, or license
+ used or accepted by some or all Allopaths
^ ancient modality (several hundred to thousands of years; the title may be modern but the practice is old)
> new modality (less than a few hundred years old)
1 mechanical/physical approach
2 mind-body approach (mind=brain)
3 non-physical approach (mind is infinite and connected to others and/or a higher consciousness)

HERBAL OR PHARMACEUTICAL TREATMENT MODALITIES

Allopathy *+>1 ("Western Medicine") includes MD's, physicians, nurses, nurse practitioners, nurse's aides, lab technicians, etc. Emphasis on pharmacology (pharmaceutical medicines) for cure and palliation. Allopathy is also listed under Physical Manipulation Modalities for surgery and injury treatment.

Naturopathy *+1^ emphasizes nutritional supplements and herbal remedies, naturally derived hormones, for prevention, cure and palliation.

Homeopathy *1> uses "reduced" prepared substances for treatment. "Like cures like".

PHYSICAL MANIPULATION MODALITIES

Allopathy *+>1 this branch of allopathy includes surgery, treatment of physical injury, physical therapy, etc.

Osteopathy *+^1 manipulation of muscle and tendon tissues, using massage, pressure points, etc. for treatment of physical injury, disability and discomfort.

Chiropractic*+>1 spinal and bone-placement adjustment for health maintenance and treatment of discomfort

Cranio-Sacral Therapy*>1 gentle manipulation of skull plates for enhancement of flow of cerebrospinal fluid

Neuro-Cranial Therapy *^1 skull plate manipulation for health maintenance and treatment

Massage *+^1 manipulation of muscle tissue to remove tension and toxins from muscles and organs, for health maintenance and treatment

Trigger-point Therapy *^1 manipulation, massage and pressure on specific points in muscles to relax them and affect relief to referred-pain areas

Rolfing *>1 manipulation of body parts to effect postural changes

<u>ENVIRONMENTAL THERAPIES</u> (changing or avoidance of external and internal environmental factors to lessen sensitivities and allergies)

Rotation diets >1 planned avoidance of certain foods at certain times, to lessen the possibility of allergic reaction (e.g. eating a certain food only once a week or every other day)

Elimination diets ^1 eliminating foods to which one has adverse reactions

Quarantine +>1 <u>A.</u> Elimination of allergy-producung or immunologic stess factors in the immediate environment of the patient; can include creation of a sterile environment, or wearing of a mask by the patient. <u>B</u>. Keeping a patient with a contagious illness out of contact with others, with special procedures for those entering and leaving, which preclude contaminations to selves, outside environments, and other people.

<u>WHOLISTIC THERAPIES</u> (Use of combinations of modalities and therapies addressing the whole bodymind organism to affect a whole treatment, and therefore opportunity for a whole cure)

Ayurveda ^1,2 diet/lifestyle system from India based on metabolic types

Chinese Medicine 1,2,3 includes some forms of massage*+^, acupuncture*+^, qigong (chi gong)^, energy work^, exercise+^, toning^, mediation+^, herbal remedies*^

RELIGION-BASED AND HOLISTIC PRACTICES

Native American Medicine ^1,2,3 includes rituals, sweats, herbs, chants, dance, smudging, etc.

Prayer +^3 petitioning of a higher source for intervention

Laying on of Hands ^3 done by a religious leader or by a group, with prayer

Curanderismo ^1,2,3 Mexican system based on Christian and pre-Christian traditions, donc by a *Curandero* or "curer".

Shamanism ^1,2,3 holistic and wholistic healing practices from several traditions, which include many other modalities on this chart.

Santeria Cubano 1,2,3 Cuban system relying on spiritism; involves unusual practices and rituals such as sacrifice; to appease "bad" spirits and call upon "good" spirits. This is a relatively modern religion-based modality that has roots in the ancient world.

Religious Ritual ^3 Rites of praise and petition for healing, from many religions, done alone or in groups

MOVEMENT-BASED SYSTEMS

Postural Re-Education *+>1 correction of posture for optimal health - Alexander Technique, Feldenkreis, etc.

Physical Therapy*+>1 manipulation and exercise education for treatment of injury, disability, and post-operative therapy

Yoga *+^1,2,3
ChiGong (Qigong) ^1,2,3
Tai Chi*^1,2,3
Use of meditative, purposeful movement to activate Chi (Qi) energy and improve health

Dance ^1
Exercise +^1
Aerobics +^1
Vigorous movement for health maintenance and improvement. Any kind of vigorous exercise is actually aerobic.

ENERGY-BASED NON-MOVEMENT MODALITIES

Intention **^3** setting the will to effect a result

Therapeutic Music/Sound:

Drumming **^2,3** use of rhythm to entrain body rhythms, produce altered states of mind, and affect physical changes

Music Practitionership, Clinical Music, Harp Therapy ***+1,2,3** Live instrumental music (and/or singing) played at the bedsides of patients, usually in medical facilities, for pain reduction, relaxation, and other healing benefits. These newly-named certified disciplines have ancient roots in the healing uses of music and sound.

Music Thanatology*+1,2,3 same as above, but specifically for the dying, in hospice settings, using harp and voice. This newly-named certified discipline has ancient roots in the use of vocal music as thanatology in Catholic monasteries.

Music Therapy *+1,2 interactive therapy through musical activity, done for groups or individuals, often for neurologic and socialization issues. This newly-named certified discipline has ancient roots in the healing uses of music and sound.

Sound Tables >1,2 tables with embedded speakers enhance the effects of sound wave frequencies on the body

Toning and Chanting ^1,2,3 using the voice as a vibrational healing/balancing tool for self or others

Vibroacoustic Harp Therapy *>1 use of a special chair that enhances the frequencies of a harp played by a trained practitioner, to magnify its effects on the body

Kinesiology*>, Polarity Therapy >1,2 uses energy-based muscle testing and energy manipulation to assess conditions and treat them

Meditation +^2,3 "emptying of the mind", or use of a mantra to calm the mind; enhances endorphin production and clarity of thinking

Biofeedback *+>2 use of electronic equipment to aid in observing the achievement of relaxation; used as therapy for migraines, chronic pain, stress reduction, etc.

Reiki *^2,3
Therapeutic Touch *+^2,3 (new name, old practice)
Touch for Health *^2,3 (new name, old practice)
External Chi Gong *^2,3
Manipulation of energy fields around the body, using the *Chi* that emanates from the hands of the practitioner

Psychoneuroimmunology+^ positive effects of the psyche on the immune system

Magnetic Field Therapy >1,2 use of magnets to manipulate energy around the body

Pranayama ^1,2 breath control for health and awareness

Non-religious ritual ^2,3 use of an activity designed to solidify an idea or desire, or produce a result

Color Therapy+^1,2 use of colored light to produce energetic and/or physical changes

Aromatherapy ^1,2 use of natural scents (such as essential oils) to affect mental, emotional, physical, or energetic change, or to enhance mood or environment

Flower Essence Therapy >3 use of essences (not essential oils) derived from plants, as tinctures taken orally, to effect states of mind

Gem/crystal therapy ^1,2 use of gems and crystals to alter of focus energy fields around the body

BEHAVIORAL THERAPIES

Psychoanalysis, Psychotherapy, Psychiatry *+>2 analytical verbal interaction

Biofeedback *+>2 use of electronic equipment to aid in observing the achievement of relaxation; used as therapy for migraines, chronic pain, stress reduction, etc.

Hypnosis *+^2 altering the state of mind (deep relaxation) for positive suggestion or recall

TREATMENTS USED IN THE PRECEDING MODALITIES

Herbs, Supplements, Essences and Medications ^:

- Ingested ^ (pills, liquids, foods, herbs, flower essences)
- Applied/absorbed ^ (creams, lotions, salves, essential oils)
- Injected *+>
- Inhaled ^(steams, sprays, aromas)
- Immersion ^(herbal baths, salt baths, hydrotherapy)

Nutrition:

- Vitamins, minerals, enzymes >
- Diet ^

Physical Manipulation ^:

movement of muscles or bone placement using the hands or mechanical equipment

Energy-Based ^:

developing energy awareness and use on self or others; manipulation of energy fields for balancing or healing

Environmental Changes ^:

Elimination of allergens or pathogens from the immediate Environment; temperature or humidity control; sound pollution control or addition of beneficial sound; light/darkness control

Cleansing:

- Colonics *+>
- Diet +^
- Herbs ^
- Fasting ^
- Laxatives+^

Surgery *+ (Allopathic)

Removal, replacement, reconstruction, or repair of internal or external body parts. Most surgerical practices are modern, but there is conclusive evidence of complex surgery in some ancient cultures.

Physical Therapy *+> (Allopathic)

Muscular/movement re-education and exercise after injury or illness, or to correct chronic or congenital problems.

Music in Medical Settings

"Pythagoras said music heals. Please keep playing." These were the words the doctor whispered to me in 1991 as I sat playing my harp for a patient in an Intensive Care Unit. Back then, live music in ICU was unheard of. There were no Music Practitioners or Clinical Musicians or Harp Therapists. There were, of course, Music Therapists[29] who did (and still do) use music as a tool in interactive therapy with clients and patients, and whose work has been well respected since the mid-1940's. But music had never been used in Intensive Care.

It happened when I got a call from my sister saying my father was in the hospital and I should come immediately. I lived far away, a 17-hour drive, and as I packed the car I thought to take my harp in case his condition was such that I would not be able to talk to him. I knew he loved my music, and it might be the only way for him to know I was there.

Upon arriving I found him hooked up to monitors, tubes and machines. He wasn't fully conscious. I asked his nurse if I could play for him, and she said, "For five minutes." After five minutes passed, no one told me to stop, so I kept going. Soon, the doctor tapped me on the shoulder and whispered the words that would change my life. *Pythagoras said music heals. Don't stop.*

When I played, the monitors showed less critical readings for his vital signs; he breathed more deeply and his pulse was more regular. Whenever I paused, alarms would buzz, and care personnel would come scurrying. So it seemed like a good idea to comply with the doctor's wishes.

The day I arrived, the family was told to prepare for the probability that my father wouldn't make it through the night. I played late into the night, and then stood at his bedside to whisper my final good-bye. I slept on a cot in his room.

When I woke in the morning, the sound of the heart monitor steadily beeping seemed the finest thing I'd ever heard - he was still alive!

As the days passed I played as much as possible, and my father improved daily. I was part of his healing team, and it appeared that my efforts were important to the medical staff. I assumed at the time that the music made a difference because I was his daughter and we therefore had a connection. But the nurses and doctors asked me to play for other patients in ICU, and there was a positive effect for them as well.

What I would never have expected was how this experience made *me* feel. Being present in a place where life was tentative and where, every minute of every day, amazing people were saving lives, gave me a sense of what's truly important in life. I felt more alive there than at any other time or place.

I stayed for a week, playing for several hours each day. The nurses and doctors told me again and again that the music was making a positive difference for the patients and for themselves as well. At the end of the week, my father was transferred to general care to complete his recovery.

As I prepared to go home, I was approached by the head nurse who asked if they could hire me. I didn't live in the area, so I declined. But since live passive music at the bedside was unknown in hospitals at the time, the request made me decide that since the medical personnel had taken my music so seriously, I would learn everything I could about how music affects the body and psyche, and how it can best be applied in medical settings.

In those days there was nothing in print about the therapeutic effects of live music for the critically ill, but I volunteered in a hospital near my home. I felt at home in medical environments, had been trained in protocols as a nurse's aide, had extensive personal experience as an inpatient, and years of playing live music in nursing homes. This background was immensely helpful.

In 1993 I was invited to start a certification program for bedside musicians. Three other musicians and I formed a nonprofit board to accomplish this. We knew that although we could teach music skills, we would have to engage medical personnel to teach clinical deportment, anatomy/physiology, basic pharmacology, monitoring, charting, infection control, and so on. We developed a stringent and responsible two-year curriculum. (We also required ourselves to take all the classes and to meet the program requirements to earn our own certifications.)

Coincidentally, two other programs emerged around the same time, and in the years that followed, several more programs were founded, and the national Standards Board for Therapeutic Music[37] was formed to develop and maintain standards for therapeutic music training programs and to define courses of study, scope of practice, a code of ethics and other rules of conduct for the certified therapeutic musician.

One of the important tasks that came up was discussion between the National Standards Board for Therapeutic Music (NSBTM) and the American Music Therapy Association[29] (AMTA) to ensure clarity on the scopes of practice between the two fields: *Music Therapy* and *therapeutic music*. (The former is a title owned by the American Music Therapy Association, and the latter includes the work of Certified Clinical Musicians, Certified Music Practitioners, Certified Harp Therapists, Certified Healing Musicians (See NSBTM[28]) and Certified Bedside Harpists[32].)

Here is a precise way to define the difference: *Music Therapy* is the use of music as a tool in interactive therapy, while *therapeutic music* uses music and only music as the therapy itself.

Service vs. Performance

Music may be offered in hospital lobbies and waiting rooms by volunteer musicians without certification. A short training may be required. Music at the bedside of a patient, however, requires certification.

Bedside music is never a performance. It is a service. The word "service" means compassionate action without agenda. It is not our job to *decide* what music the patient needs; instead we *observe* what their musical needs may be. That makes the difference between being of service and being a thorn in the side of the recipient.

We can't decide before entering the room exactly what we are going to play for a patient or for how long. We observe a patient's musical needs by watching body language, breathing, and vital signs indicated on monitors. Sometimes we use intuition as well. (Asking what someone's favorite music is may be appropriate if the patient is aware, awake, and not otherwise engaged; but be aware that just entertaining them is not our goal.) We might ask whether quiet or cheerful music, in low or high pitches, is preferred.

We must never ask a patient about their medical condition or treatment (not only because it's rude, but also because it's illegal). In some hospitals or hospices we might have access to their charts, and can get information from that source that can help us determine what kinds of music may be beneficial. But in all cases, the patient's status in the present moment is what we ultimately use to make this decision.

In the application of therapeutic music, when we focus our attention on the patient, this allows the patient to focus their attention inward. When they know that they are not expected to focus on the musician, the result is deeply relaxing and promotes production of endorphins, alleviating the awareness of pain and/or anxiety, and enhancing immune response.

Music as a service at the bedside transforms the experience of illness or dying, it connects the patient with another person even though he or she may not be able to interact, it calms, it provides a pleasant atmosphere for the hospital staff and for the patient's family (if present), it is an act of compassion and caring, and it provides a humane element in a sterile environment. Therapeutic musicians are redefining the paradigm of institutionalized care, and helping to enhance the image and practice of modern medicine.

By the way, many therapeutic musicians report a complete cessation of "stage fright" while playing at the bedsides of patients. When you focus on the patient instead of yourself, fear of failure becomes impossible.

Intention

An oft-heard discussion regarding our work as therapeutic musicians involves the term "intention", which might be defined as envisioning your music having specific effects, or a decision about exactly what the music session will accomplish. Intention is a much misunderstood concept.

One of the pitfalls of sending intention through our will is that it produces a sense of well-being in us that we can misconstrue as an indication that what we are doing is the right thing. In actuality, this sensation can occur regardless of whether the mind is in a state of grace or a state of ego! To cite an example:

When I was a child, I was taught to give away things I cherished. When I did, it gave me a great sense of self-satisfaction, and it felt good. It was not until many years later that I realized that people don't necessarily want what I cherish; they want what *they* cherish. A true gift is one that is given regardless of how it makes *me* feel.

When we play music at the bedside, true intention means that what we do is for the good of the patient, whatever that may be, regardless of our own sense of satisfaction or importance.

Dr. Larry Dossey has done a great deal of research showing that directed intention has real and measurable effects, and that deciding what we think is best for someone is where we can run into trouble. (These concepts are introduced in the earlier books, and explored more fully in the latter ones; all are listed at the end of this article.)

It's not how strong our will is, but how effective out music is, that is the basis of our work. When it comes to patients, are we not first and foremost bedside *musicians*? Don't we trust the *music* to do the job? If we don't, why bother playing music at all? If we think live music is not capable of doing the job, we have not been educated in the physical, emotional, and spiritual effects of live music that prove it to be a modality that has its own complete integrity. Music itself contains the healing ingredients.

This does not negate the spiritual aspects of music; quite the opposite. We can look at music in a purely scientific way <u>and</u> we can marvel at how its resonant complexities produce results that are somehow greater than science.

The essence of intention is *knowing* that our work will be of benefit; we express that knowing by showing up, deporting ourselves responsibly, and playing appropriate music. This is simple, elegant, and involves no claim of special powers. It is fine to use a meditative, prayerful, or focused state of mind to help us in our work, but beyond that, let's keep our intention simple and let the *music* do the healing. True intention is actually trust. Trust requires no concern that we must somehow force our music to be effective.

No Credit – No Blame

If we are doing our work with integrity but the response we get seems negative, it makes no sense to take blame for it. That said, we *are* responsible for playing well and playing appropriate music for our patients. If you have not developed your music skills sufficiently, and/or have not learned what types and tempos of music to play for which kinds of patients, inappropriate music *could* actually do harm.

When something good happens, we can allow ourselves to feel good about it. But we can't own full credit for it. Taking credit for a good outcome is actually a burden, because it sets up an expectation that we can make it happen again in the future. If it doesn't, we may think we've failed. Most often, a patient ultimately responds to a combination of modalities, and the addition of music to the care they are already receiving may be the icing on the cake to produce a positive effect.

Simple vs. Complex Music

Most healthcare music is simple in structure and arrangement. Complex music is excellent for stage performances, but it is not used in medical settings. (It's unfortunate that some good musicians who are not trained in therapeutic applications tend to play complex music for patients, and the effects are rarely positive. Keep it simple! This is about *helping the patients*, not impressing them with your skills.)

Keep in mind that "simple" doesn't mean "poorly played". One must have good skills to make simple music sound well.

Sometimes, those who are healthy may remark that therapeutic music is boring and repetitive. Yes, to healthy people, it is! But to the very sick, it is a relief and a blessing. It is the resonance rather than the entertainment value that is important.

In many situations, family members of the patient may be present and may expect entertainment. We explain that the style of music we're playing is for a specific therapeutic purpose, and might offer to play for the family later in a waiting room or lounge area. If, however, the patient is awake and aware, in certain situations we may entertain them and their family together.

Healing or Curing?

Healing and curing are not synonymous. Medical personnel often take issue with the idea that music heals. What they mean is that it cannot be claimed that music *cures*.

Curing is the eradication of physical illness or injury. Healing is the return to or the attaining of a sense of wholeness of mind and spirit. I have seen healing happen in the absence of cure, and I have seen curing take place after healing, but I have never seen permanent cure occur without prior healing.

When asked by a doctor or other health care professional why music is effective, it's sufficient to explain that music is a noninvasive and unobtrusive modality which has been shown to reduce awareness of pain, is relaxing to the patient, and promotes better sleep.

You can also quote some of the research on its effects. Research on therapeutic music is proliferating so fast it's not practical to cite even a small percentage of it here, but any search of the Web will turn up a great deal of it. Also see the websites of the National Standards Board for Therapeutic Music[37] and the American Music Therapy Association[29].

Clinical Deportment and Ethics

The majority of musicians who are interested in playing at patients' bedsides in hospitals and hospices love the idea of the warm, person-to-person, spiritual and communicative aspects of the work. It's easy to assume that clinical deportment, legal issues, procedures, codes, and ethics aren't important. One could not be more mistaken. In a hospital, there is more than just caring *about* the patients - there is caring *for* the patients. Protocols exist to ensure that each patient gets the best care, and *everyone* who works or volunteers in a medical environment must comply.

For those who have not spent much time inside clinical environments, it can come as a surprise that what is considered polite and appropriate behavior in the outside world is not always the same in a hospital or hospice. Making a faux pas in the outside world is embarrassing, but making one in a hospital can be dangerous or even lethal to someone.

For a reality check on what is and is not appropriate deportment in a medical environment, here are a few true/false exercises. They are representative of the kinds of things you need to know.

1. Nurses always appreciate a friendly conversation.
   __True __False

2. You can provide relief to hospice caregivers by staying with a patient while they take a break. __True __False

3. You can be of service to patients when they ask for your assistance with things such as a glass of water, fluffing the pillow, opening a window, shifting position, and so on.
   __True __False

4. You should always have access to patients' charts.
__True __False

5. You have a right to know the patient's condition and medical history. __True __False

6. You may ask caregivers and visitors to leave the room when you play for the patient. __True __False

7. You may invite others into the patient's room to hear your music. __True __False

8. You can ask the patient to sing along or clap along to your music. __True __False

9. You may set up and play anywhere in the room.
__True __False

10. Staff members or patients' family members will help you get in and out of doors and set up or take down your equipment.
__True __False

11. The medical staff is there to provide for your needs so you can do your work. __True __False

12. Sharing your personal history and concerns with your patients makes them feel more comfortable with you.
__True __False

13. It's good to share with your family and friends who you played for and what transpired. __True __False

14. If someone is sleeping when you arrive, you may wake them up. __True __False

15. You may offer your opinion on diagnosis to a patient or their caregiver. __True __False

16. You may call yourself by any title you wish. __True __False

17. You don't have to wear an I.D. badge. __True __False

18. You don't have to check in at the nurse's station every time you go to the hospital to play. __True __False

19. No one has the right to ask you to leave. __True __False

20. You don't have to stop playing if the patient or the family asks you to. __True __False

<u>ANSWERS:</u> The answer to every one of the above is FALSE. If you were mistaken about one or more of them, you can see how important it is to be trained. Before learning why, many good-hearted people disagree with some of these answers, and if you do, that is further indication that opportunities for discussion are important. All healthcare music training programs focus on these issues.

You may also be required to take an orientation at the hospital or hospice that accepts you. And you will probably get a TB test, a badge, a parking permit, and so on. Consider this a good thing.

Your Appearance and What it Says

For much of my life, I dressed "artistically". I felt strongly that it was a means of self-expression. It told the world I was creative.

When I first worked in a hospital (as a nurse's aide) I hated how my uniform made me feel. My outward statement of individuality was gone. People would have to get to know me to find out who I was. I had a hard time reconciling that, while at work, my role was "aide", not "artist".

I often run into this with musicians in hospital and hospice settings. Not accustomed to thinking of themselves as clinicians, they show up in all kinds of interesting garb. In a clinical environment, this is not what wins serious consideration by administrators and staff. "When in Rome, do as the Romans do" is a famous saying for a reason.

I recommend businesslike clothing in plain, pastel colors without large patterns. A neat shirt, jacket, slacks and shoes that are comfortable will send a message of friendliness, are easy on patient's eyes, and practical as well. Black, red, and white are avoided. No flowing or very short skirts, open sandals, spike heels, sparkly stuff, sportswear, hats, fringes, see-through materials, and so on.

Therapeutic musicians simply cannot afford to be seen as anything less than professional. In this developing field, we do not want to be left behind merely because we could not show respect for the medical professions by dressing appropriately.

Terminology of Healthcare Music

“therapeutic musician” or “healing musician”: an informal way of referring to Music Practitioners, Music Therapists, Clinical Musicians, Harp Thanatologists, Harp Practitioners, and Certified Clinical Musicians. (These titles may not be used by uncertified musicians.) *It should be ascertained whether someone calling themselves a therapeutic musician or a healing musician is actually trained and certified.*

harp therapist: A term used by some harpists doing therapeutic music; may or may not be certified.

“healthcare music” - live music offered by a certified musician (or intern) in a medical setting.

“vigil”: The attendance of a clinical musician at the bedside of a dying *patient during the actual death process and/or through death* (music session at the bedside is not otherwise a vigil).

“bedside music”: a non-interactive session of live music by a certified clinical musician or practitioner at the bedside in a hospital or hospice.

“performance”**:** A concert or entertainment; *not* a therapeutic music session.

Using Modes

The use of specific modes is sometimes suggested for specific healing purposes. It is said that certain modes promote well-being, due to unique combinations of frequencies in their intervals.

Over many years of playing for patients, I have observed the results of modal music therapies and have noted some interesting outcomes. First a bit of personal history: although I am presently more broad in my philosophic outlook, I grew up in the Catholic Church before Vatican II, when Medieval modal music was used extensively in worship. I loved this music and still respond to the Medieval modes. I find them peaceful, introspective, and evocative of deeper states of consciousness. I am not, however, in the majority.

Although modal music was both religious and secular (popular) in the Middle Ages, that was four hundred years ago and more, and those who are not musicologists, older Catholics, or music school graduates are not likely to have been exposed to it. To many people, especially non-musicians, these modes can sound eerie, uncomfortable, and depressing. Claims of the healing nature of the less familiar modes originated during the Middle Ages, and have never been proven by scientific method. For those who find them disturbing, they are obviously not therapeutic. Modes should be used judiciously.

A mode is a scale based on the diatonic scale but which begins on a note other than the tonic of the diatonic scale. There are seven modes (in order of their starting notes, they are Ionian, Dorian, Phrygian, Lydian, Mixolydian, Aeolian, and Locrian) and each has a different "personality".

The following chart explains:

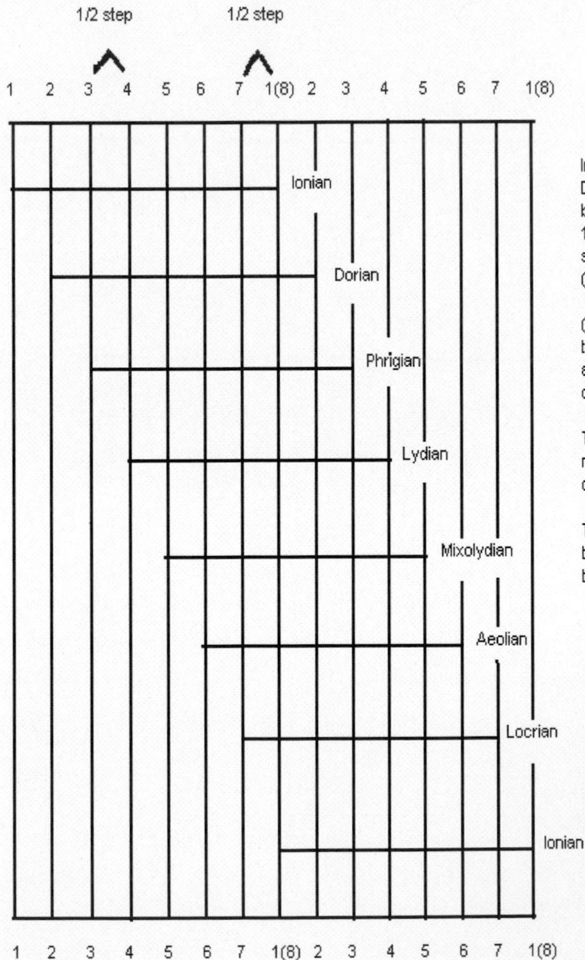

In any key, the notes of the Diatonic (do-re-mi) scale can be numbered: 1,2,3,4,5,6,7, and 1 or 8, as shown on the chart. The tonic (first note) of the scale is 1.

(For instance, in the key of C, the notes are C,D,E,F,G,A,B,C, and the C note is 1. In the key of G, the G note is 1. Etc.)

The vertical lines represent notes. This chart shows two octaves.

The horizontal llines represent the names of the modes and the range of each mode.

Note that in the diatonic scale there are two half step locations, between notes 3 and 4 and between notes 7 and 8. The locations of the half steps do not change, but since the modes begin in different positions, the half steps factor differently in each mode. It is this shift of half steps that creates the typical sound of each mode.

It's easy to learn modes by their numbers:

Ionian - the 1 mode - goes from the tonic (1) note up the successive notes to its octave, or, to put it very simply, from 1 to 8. You can demonstrate this by playing from C to C on the white keys of a piano (or the strings of a harp tuned to C) and saying the number of the note as you play it, "1,2,3,4,5,6,7,8". If you say the *name* of the note, as in C,D,E, etc. you will confuse yourself because the principle of modes is not dependent on the note names, but on their relative *positions*, or numbers.

Dorian - the 2 mode - goes from the second note (2) up to its octave, or from 2 to 2. Start on the 2 note (i.e. D) and say the note names as you play them, "2,3,4,5,6,7,1,2"

Phrygian - the 3 mode - goes from the third note (3) up to its octave, or from 3 to 3. Start on the 3 note (i.e. E) and say the note names as you play them, "3,4,5,6,7,1,2,3"

...and so on with each mode:

Lydian - the 4 mode
Mixolydian - the 5 mode
Aeolean - the 6 mode
Locrian - the 7 mode

What make a modal a mode is that the half steps change position successively in each modal scale. You can start in any key; the modes retain their numbers regardless of key. For instance, in the key of C, C is 1; In the key of G, G is 1; and so on.

The Ionian and Aeolian modes are the ones we westerners hear most often in popular music. The Mixolydian and Dorian modes are often heard in Celtic music. The Dorian and the remaining modes are often heard in Medieval music.

Other Scales

There are always cultural considerations when we play for patients. If awake and aware, they need music they can relate to. For instance, when I worked in a hospital where a large percentage of patients were American Indian, I found that about half of the indigenous patients asked for hymns, and the rest preferred Native flute music or country songs with guitar, but did not enjoy the harp or violin. Likewise, other patients who grew up outside the western hemisphere preferred music from their own cultures.

There are several ethnic scales that are useful when called for:

The scales below are indicated in the key of C. The same scale intervals can be achieved in other keys by transposing, of course.

<u>Whole-tone Pentatonic</u> = CDEFGA - a five-note scale that is very useful for easy improvisation and glissandos. On a harp, this can be achieved by lifting the 3rd and 7th levers of the scale, which will produce some duplicate notes so you don't have to avoid them. On a piano it can be achieved by playing only the black keys: C# D# F# G# A#. On a flute, simply avoid the 3rd and 7th notes of the diatonic scale.

Oriental = DFGAC
African and Greek = DEGAB
Egyptian = FGABC
Swedish = A B C# D E F G
Hebrew = B C D# E F# G A

(In some ethnic music, there are scales that contain more than twelve tones. For instance, in some Middle Eastern and Oriental scales there can be as many as four notes in the space we think of as one step. Obviously, we can't reproduce this music on instruments that play only naturals, sharps and flats.)

Current Philosophies of Healthcare Music

Appropriate Instruments

Although several of the training programs are for harp players, harps are not the only therapeutic instruments. There are even times when certain patients do not respond well to harps, for whatever reason (occasionally the association with angels is a problem), and a different instrument may work better. Please see the list of instruments in my book *Composing Therapeutic Music*[42].

High and Low Pitch

It's generally agreed that an instrument capable of producing low tones is therapeutically preferable. Most adult patients respond well to pleasant low tones from acoustic instruments. However, sometimes, for reasons of practicality, therapeutic musicians have to choose small portable instruments with limited ranges. It's a necessary compromise. The only time a small instrument is inappropriate for bedside music is when its volume is too soft to be heard clearly a few feet away, or its pitch is so high as to be annoying. On the other hand, any instrument that is so large as to get in the way or produce too much volume is not appropriate.

By the way, "therapy harp" is a popular term for certain small harps that are made to be very portable. A 'therapy harp" is not the only kind of harp that is suited to therapeutic playing. It is merely a term used by harpmakers.

Acoustic vs. Electric and Electronic Music

An acoustic instrument is any instrument that is not amplified. No electric cords are attached to it.

The principle of acoustic instruments lies in a hollow chamber called a soundbox or sounding chamber. With stringed instruments, the soundbox is part of the instrument itself.

There are four factors in the production of acoustic sound production:

- the *sounding chamber*
- the *vibratory element*
- the *energy source*
- the *manipulative source*

In stringed instruments, the *energy source* is the hands of the player, which pluck, bow, fret, and/or strike the strings. In wind instruments, the energy source is the breath of the player. In acoustic keyboard instruments, there is an extra mechanical element that strikes the strings when the fingers depress the keys.

For any of these acoustic instruments, the *manipulative source* is the hands. (Therefore the hands are both energy source and manipulative source for stringed instruments.)

The *vibratory elements* of a stringed instrument are, of course, the strings. For wind instruments, it is the reed and/or the body of the instrument. With any acoustic instrument, it isn't possible to separate the vibratory element from the sounding chamber, because the entire sounding chamber also vibrates.

Looking at a guitar, violin, or cello, one sees an hourglass-shaped body with a long neck, upon which strings are attached. The neck is for manipulation of the strings. The body (soundbox) is the *sounding chamber* which enhances the vibration of the strings.

When a string is bowed or plucked, it vibrates at a certain frequency depending on its length, tension, material, and thickness. The vibration, of course, produces sound. The sound waves bounce back and forth on the inside surface of the sounding chamber, which in turn is thereby set into motion. You then have not just a vibrating string but an entire vibrating instrument. Additionally, the other strings often respond by vibrating sympathetically, thus further increasing the richness of the sound.

Not only is vibration (sound) transferred through the air into the sounding chamber, but also through solid material connecting the strings to the soundbox (sounding chamber). The exact size and construction of the soundbox, and the material from which it is made, determine the potential volume and tone quality of the instrument. The player's skill also determines tone quality, of course.

The places where sound emerges from an acoustic instrument are commonly called *sound holes*. Their size, placement, and shape also effect tone and volume. A smaller hole will enhance the bass range of an instrument, while a larger one will enhance the treble range. However, too large a hole, or too many holes, will open up the sound chamber too much, defeating its purpose, as there won't be enough enclosed space for sound waves to bounce around.

A flute or oboe has almost no sounding chamber. One might wonder how it produces any volume. Anyone who has tried to play one knows that blowing hard is not the answer. The secret lies within the body of the player. The instrument by itself is incomplete until the player adds the open spaces of his or her own sinus cavities, throat, trachea and lungs. When these are kept open through careful manipulation of related musculature one can achieve good tone and volume with a small wind instrument. The tone enhanced by the body of the player is transferred back to the instrument and then out to the listener.

The tone quality of an acoustic instrument is rich with harmonics (overtones) produced from all the vibration described above. Even one note contains more overtones than can be detected in the range of human hearing. These resonances run the complete spectrum of frequency that the human body thrives upon. Therefore, acoustic instruments are perfect for therapy.

Some instruments rest against bony structures of the body, such as the sternum or clavicle, better conducting sound into the body. It has been surmised this has a direct effect on the thymus gland which resides under the sternum, and which is important to the immune system. Of course, this and many other factors make the sound of your own musical instrument self-therapeutic.

While acoustic instruments produce complex sound waves, while electronic ones usually produce a single sine wave per note. Even with a Midi keyboard, which uses sounds recorded from other instruments and which therefore may have some harmonic richness, you can still hear a lack of overtones because the sound is compressed.

Some say that a pure sine wave is the most therapeutic. Theoretically, it could target a very specific part of the body, and if we knew exactly what its effect would be, that could have measurable applications. But we cannot know specifically what the effect of any pure sound is on an individual. We can see the effects of pure frequencies on nonliving matter, scar tissue, and on viruses and bacteria, and we know that the same tone always produces the same Cymatic pattern in controlled experiments. But with complex living organisms, the matter being affected is always diverse, and for each person, plant, or animal, the same tone can have somewhat different effects. This is why harmonic richness is important. The more overtones, the wider the therapeutic "range of coverage". (To understand the physical differences from one person to another that can affect the application of tone, consider that every person has different amounts of adipose tissue and different bone density. Those factors alone can be significant.)

In my experience, the length of time a patient is able to tolerate an electronic instrument is much shorter than an acoustic one, and agitation is less prevalent when acoustic instruments are used.

Acoustic instruments with an added amplifier are not preferable to purely acoustic sound. Some of the acoustic frequencies will emanate from the instrument itself, but most of the sound will go through the amplifier and its quality will be compromised. It is a rare amplifier that can reproduce acoustic quality accurately, and even more rare for a player to keep the volume at a reasonable level. Never use an amplifier in therapeutic situations, except in elder homes where hearing loss is an issue and you are an *entertainer*.

This is a good place to offer some interesting information about Muzak. An environment imbued with the sounds of Muzak is little better than one with no music at all. "Muzak" is an electronically compressed and equalized recording of generic popular melodies, from which harmonic complexity has been removed. It is commonly assumed that Muzak exists to enhance the environment, but in most cases it has an agitating effect, which is its actual purpose. This is why it's often used in restaurants; it makes people eat faster, so the turnover of customers is greater, bringing in more profit. In elevators and lobbies it keeps people from lingering. Muzak is currently used in some shopping-center parking lots at night to keep gangs from loitering there. It has its uses, but therapeutics is not one of them. It's very unfortunate that some hospitals, quite innocently, use it in an attempt to enhance the atmosphere!

On the other hand, children and teens who study in classrooms where pleasant, good quality recorded music is played have been seen to achieve better retention of information and score better in tests than do those who study without pleasant music. (Studying with rap, punk, or rock music is counterproductive.)

The Human Voice

Think of the human body as an acoustic instrument. The vocal cords are the strings; the mouth, sinuses, throat, trachea, and lungs are the sounding chamber; the breath is the energy source; and the musculature is the manipulative source. All these parts work together to produce a sound like no other instrument, and each individual voice is unlike any other.

We can all learn how to use our vocal instrument to its best advantage. A beautiful voice is not necessarily something we are born with - we have to learn how to use it just as we would learn how to play any other instrument. If anyone has told you that your voice isn't "good enough", they are probably wrong. You couldn't expect to pick up a cello and play it beautifully without taking lessons. The same is true for the voice. Most of us can have beautiful voices, and you are no exception.

Like a flute, blowing hard does not produce good tone, but opening up the sounding chambers within the body produces good tone, volume, and projection. And practice is essential to develop those skills.

Our voice is our most intimate instrument, and in using it we display who we are. Our voices reflect our inner selves so thoroughly that even what we don't know about ourselves comes out for others to hear. This is especially true of the untrained voice. With training one learns how to bypass the effects of one's physical, emotional, mental, and psychological states. But by using those techniques and thereby changing the voice, one also changes oneself! One thing cannot change without the other following after. Our voice is our innate doctor.

Good voice teachers know to be careful and considerate of the intricate and fragile nature of the personality and psyche behind the voice they are training. If your voice teacher is compassionate but also prods you beyond what you think your limits are, you have a good teacher.

One of the most compelling reasons to use your voice is for your own benefit, both because it feels good psychologically, but also because it has physical effects. The vibrations produced by your own voice are largely responsible for production and flow of cerebro-spinal fluid. It also effects endorphin production. The delicate structures of the inner ear are kept in good working order by these vibrations as well. With the addition of the many other benefits of therapeutic sound that we have already discussed in this book, it's obvious that singing and toning are profoundly self-therapeutic.

Improvisational Music

Being able to improvise is an important skill in therapeutic music. Improvisation means playing without pre-planning, rather than playing specific known compositions. Some students are afraid it will be difficult, when in fact improvisation is one of the easiest of musical skills.

Improvisation can be as easy as tuning your instrument to an open tuning and playing random notes. Or it can be done from a place of intimate familiarity with music theory. It can be done rhythmically or non-rhythmically, and in any mood, key and tempo. A good class in improvisation will open many doors.

“Improv” is what we do when:

- We need to segue between pieces without stopping
- There is nothing in our usual repertoire that feels right to play at a particular moment or in a particular situation
- What the patient needs is music they won’t recognize
- We are momentarily distracted
- We don’t have an arrangement for a requested tune, and need to approximate it
- We run out of repertoire
- It feels like the right thing to do

Closing Remarks

Now that you have read this book, remember that knowing *about* something is not the same as learning through experience and putting one's knowledge it into practice. We become experts through what we do rather than what we know about.

In the early 1990's when live music as a passive therapy for hospital and hospice patients was a new idea, what we practitioners saw in those first years astonished us. And the wonder has never ceased. We did and still do see patients emerge from comas, head trauma patients and stroke patients and Alzheimer's patients speak or sing after months or years of silence, minimally active people get up and dance, screaming children fall asleep, and unresponsive people smile. We see their families form new bonds, express their feelings, relax their stress. We are told again and again how valued we are by clinical staff.

Back then I thought our biggest challenge would be to gain acceptance in allopathic medical settings. But soon therapeutic musicians were welcomed nearly everywhere. In fact, the biggest challenge now is to train enough certified therapeutic musicians to meet the growing demand.

Therapeutic musicians, Music Therapists and sound healers must acknowledge the differences in each others' work, and be sure medical personnel and private clientele are accurately informed about them. We can and must support each other in this effort. We each have different functions and are not in competition.

We can each do our part in contributing to the advancement of musical in clinical, private, and public settings, we can develop community activities based on musical participation, we can involve children by volunteering in schools, and we can make music for ourselves and our families. We all need more music in our lives.

Endnotes

1. Don Campbell: www.mozarteffect.com
2. *Singing the Universe Awake:* laurieriley.com/books.htm
3. Julie Lyon Lieberman:
www.julielyonn.com/frames.php?page=books&menu=corne
4. *The Harper's Manual:* laurieriley.com/books.htm
5. Alexander Technique: www.alexandertechnique.com
6. Healing and the Mind: www.ambrosevideo.com/items.cfm?id=376
Bill Moyers: www.lucidcafe.com/library/96jun/moyers.html
7. Candace Pert: www.candacepert.com
8. Byron Katie: www.thework.com/index.asp
Loving What Is: http://www.amazon.com/Loving-What-Four-Questions-Change/dp/0609608746
9. Feldenkreis Method:
altmedicine.about.com/od/therapiesfrometol/a/Feldenkrais.htm
10. Robert Hooke: www.gap-system.org/~history/Biographies/Hooke.html
11. Ernst Chladni: http://en.wikipedia.org/wiki/Ernst_Chladni
12. Hans Jenny: http://en.wikipedia.org/wiki/Hans_Jenny_(cymatics)
Cymatics: http://www.cymaticsource.com
13. Dr. Masaru Emoto: http://en.wikipedia.org/wiki/Masaru_Emoto
14. Gabor Forgacs:
www.physics.missouri.edu/people/faculty/GaborForgacs.html
15. Barbara Hero: www.lambdoma.com/barbara-hero.php
16. Jonathan Goldman: www.healingsounds.com/biography.asp
17: Kay Gardner: http://en.wikipedia.org/wiki/Kay_Gardner_(composer)
18. Nikola Tesla: www.neuronet.pitt.edu/~bogdan/tesla/bio.htm
19. Tacoma Narrows Bridge:
http://en.wikipedia.org/wiki/Tacoma_Narrows_Bridge AND
www.youtube.com/watch?v=ASd0t3n8Bnc
20. Joshua Leeds: www.joshualeeds.com/
21. Margo Drohan: http://chp.sagepub.com/cgi/reprint/5/1/25 .
22. Broken Heart Syndrome: http://www.hopkinsmedicine.org/press_releases/2005/02_10_05.html)
23. Psychoneuroimmonology:
http://en.wikipedia.org/wiki/Psychoneuroimmunology
24. Ranjie Singh: http://www.7dhealth.com/earticles
25. Elizabeth Kubler Ross – five stage of grief:
http://www.businessballs.com/elisabeth_kubler_ross_five_stages_of_grief.htm
26. Dr. John Beaulieu: www.healingmusic.org/hmo/JohnBeaulieu/index.asp
27. Dr. Larry Dossey: www.dosseydossey.com/larry/default.html
28. National Standards Board for Therapeutic Music:
http://www.therapeuticmusician.com
Books by Dr. Larry Dossey:

- *Healing Words*
- *Healing Beyond the Body*
- *Reinventing Medicine*
- *Prayer is Good Medicine*
- *Be Careful What You Pray For*
- *Meaning and Medicine*
- *Recovering the Soul*
- *Space, Time and Medicine*

29. American Music Therapy Association: http://www.musictherapy.org
30. Stella Benson: www.healersway.com/
31. Christina Tourin: www.emeraldharp.com/
32. Edie Elkan: www.bedsideharp.com
33. Dr. Oliver Sacks: www.oliversacks.com/about-the-author/biography
34. Clinical Musicians Program: developed by Laurie Riley and now administrated by Dee Sweeney at www.harpforhealing.com
35. Kylea Taylor: http://kyleataylor.com
36. Music for Healing and Transition Program: www.mhtp.org
37. National Standards Board for Therapeutic Music http://www.therapeuticmusician.com/
38. Benoit Mandelbrot (*The Fractal Geometry of Nature, 1982* and *Fractals: Form, Chance and Dimension, 1977*), Professor of Mathematical Sciences Emeritus at Yale University; IBM Fellow Emeritus at the Thomas J. Watson Research Center; and Battelle Fellow at the Pacific Northwest National Laboratory.
39. Marianne Williamson: http://en.wikiquote.org/wiki/Marianne_Williamson
40. *Racketeering in Medicine: The Suppression of Alternatives* James P. Carter
41. Folk Harp Journal http://www.folkharpsociety.org/pages/journal.html
42. *Composing Healthcare Music*: see www.laurieriley.com

About the Author

Laurie Riley, CMP*, CCM* is a professional musician who tours internationally to speak, teach, and perform. Her pioneering work in the field of healthcare music included founding the Clinical Musicians' training program[34], co-founding the Music for Healing and Transition Program[36], and developing music programs in hospices and hospitals. She has trained hundreds of therapeutic musicians.

Laurie is a popular keynote speaker for conferences and events. A number of Laurie's students have become well-known authors, presenters, program directors, and performers as well.

Laurie plays and teaches a variety of instruments including harp and guitar, and is also a vocalist. Having recorded over a dozen albums of harp music, she has also authored numerous instructional books for musicians, as well as DVD's.

Besides Body, Mind and Music, her books written specifically for therapeutic musicians include Composing Healthcare Music, How to Start a Music Program in Your Local Hospital or Hospice, and Play the Therapy Harp. They are available at www.laurieriley.com (along with her many instructional materials specifically for harpists).

*CMP: Certified Music Practitioner
*CCM: Certified Clinical Musician

Laurie can be contacted at laurie.riley@live.com